THE BIG BOOK
OF PETS

THE BIG BOOK
OF PETS

COMPILED AND EDITED BY

MARGARET GREEN

PICTURES BY

JANUSZ

GRABIANSKI

MULBERRY BOOKS

ACKNOWLEDGMENTS

The editor and the publisher have made every effort to trace the ownership of all material contained herein. It is their belief that the necessary permissions from publishers, authors, and authorized agents have been obtained in all cases. In the event of any question arising as to the use of any material, the editor and publisher, while expressing regret for any error unconsciously made, will be pleased to make the necessary correction in future editions of this book. Thanks are due to the following authors, publishers, publications, and agents for permission to use the material indicated.

"Rascal," by Sterling North, from the book RASCAL, by Sterling North. Copyright © 1963 by Sterling North. Reprinted by permission of E. P. Dutton & Co., Inc.

"The Christmas Pony," by Lincoln Steffens, from the book BOY ON HORSEBACK, by Lincoln Steffens. Copyright 1931, 1935 by Harcourt, Brace & World, Inc.; renewed © 1959, 1963 by Peter Steffens. Reprinted by permission of the publishers.

"Grishka's Bear," by René Guillot. Copyright 1960 by Criterion Books, Inc. Reprinted by permission of the publisher from GRISHKA AND THE BEAR, by René Guillot (New York: 1960). Reprinted also by permission of Oxford University Press.

"Ricotte," by Colette, from the book CREATURES GREAT AND SMALL, by Colette. Reprinted by permission of Farrar, Straus & Giroux, Inc. and Martin Secker & Warburg, Ltd., London. First published in the U. S. A. 1957.

"Kate's Froggery," by Kate Douglas Wiggin, from the book MY GARDEN OF MEMORY, by Kate Douglas Wiggin. Reprinted by permission of Houghton Mifflin Co.

"Elsa Goes to the Indian Ocean," by Joy Adamson, from the book BORN FREE, by Joy Adamson. © Copyright 1960 by Joy Adamson. Reprinted by permission of Pantheon Books, Division of Random House, Inc., and William Collins Sons & Co. Canada Ltd., Toronto and London.

"Miss Nightingale's Pets," by Cecil Woodham-Smith, from the book FLORENCE NIGHTINGALE, by Cecil Woodham-Smith. Used by permission of McGraw-Hill Book Company and Constable Publishers.

"Chut, the Kangaroo," by Dorothy Cottrell, from the book WILDERNESS ORPHAN, by Dorothy Cottrell. Reprinted by permission of Paul R. Reynolds, Inc.

"Mr. Cat Disappears," by George Freedley, from the book MR. CAT, by George Freedley. Copyright 1960 by George Freedley, published by Howard Frisch, 114 Christopher Street, New York 10014. Reprinted by permission.

"Wol Helps Out," by Farley Mowat, from the book OWLS IN THE FAMILY, by Farley Mowat. Copyright © 1961 by Farley Mowat. Reprinted by permission of Atlantic-Little, Brown and Co.

"The Easter Lamb," by An Rutgers van der Loeff, from the book STEFFOS AND HIS EASTER LAMB. Reprinted by permission of the University of London Press, Ltd.

"Magnus and the Squirrel," by Hans Peterson, from the book MAGNUS AND THE SQUIRREL, by Hans Peterson, Copyright © 1959 by The Viking Press, Inc. Reprinted by permission of The Viking Press, Inc.

"Too Many Kittens," by Helen Hoke. © 1947 by Helen Hoke.

"The Little Prisoner," by Grey Owl, reprinted with the permission of Charles Scribner's Sons, Peter Davies Ltd. The Estate of Grey Owl, and The Macmillan Co. of Canada Ltd., from SAJO AND THE BEAVER PEOPLE, by Grey Owl. Copyright 1936 by Grey Owl; renewal copyright © 1964 Canada Permanent Toronto General Trust Co.

"Platero and I," by Juan Ramón Jiménez, from the book PLATERO AND I, by Juan Ramón Jiménez, translated by Eloise Roach. University of Texas Press, Austin, 1957.

"Foxy," by John Montgomery, from the book FOXY, by John Montgomery. Copyright © 1959 by John Montgomery. Reprinted by permission, Franklin Watts, Inc.

"Dinah Was a Mantis," by Edwin Way Teale, reprinted by permission of Dodd, Mead & Company from STRANGE LIVES OF FAMILIAR INSECTS, by Edwin Way Teale. Copyright © 1962 by Edwin Way Teale.

"The Rescue," by H. Mortimer Batten. Reprinted from THE SINGING FOREST by permission of Farrar, Straus & Giroux, Inc. and Charles Lavell Ltd. Copyright © 1964 by Farrar, Straus & Co., Inc.

"The Goshawk," by T. H. White. Reprinted from THE GOSHAWK, published by Jonathan Cape. Reprinted by permission of International Authors N. V.

"Koka the Cockatoo," by Konrad Lorenz, from the book KING SALOMON'S RING, by Konrad Lorenz. Reprinted by permission of Methuen & Company, London.

"Badger Brock," by Lilli Koenig, from the book TALES FROM THE VIENNA WOODS, by Lilli Koenig. Reprinted by permission of Methuen & Company, London.

Library of Congress Catalog Card Number: 66-15975

Editorial arrangement and commentary © 1966 by
Margaret Green

Illustrations copyright © 1966 by Carl Ueberreuter
Druck und Verlag (M. Salzer), Vienna, Austria

Printed in Austria

SBN 531-02050-9

CONTENTS

ABOUT THIS BOOK

The stories in this collection, although as varied as the animals themselves, have in common that special relationship of trust, affection, and dependence between a human and an animal which entitles us to call the animal a pet. These stories are of real animals — not animals that talk, nor beasts with magical powers, but creatures that live with people and, for a while at least, share their lives.

Some of the stories like "Platero and I" and "Ricotte" describe everyday events; some — "Wol Helps Out" and "Koka the Cockatoo" for example — relate farcical incidents; others bring a lump to the throat, among them "Chut, the Kangaroo", "The Little Prisoner" and "Foxy", for the way their owners defend their pets' very lives after unjust accusation or provocation and for the bewildered animal in alien surroundings; still others reach to the extremes of sacrifice in high drama as "The Rescue" or "Grishka's Bear".

Although the onus is firmly on the owner to care for his pet — and he must be prepared to go to all limits to do so whether he is a Mr. Freedley in his sophisticated New York apartment or a Steffos in his primitive Greek village — the return which the pet makes may be no less great. Meli is given new hope of life through the trust which the sick animals show in her; the Captain's wife grows in understanding and tolerance through the loyalty of her husband's dog, Zero; David discovers the real feeling of having his own family through his foster parents' understanding over Foxy.

Antoine de Saint-Exupéry, in his book, *The Little Prince*, describes the essence of the relationship when he makes the wild fox explain to the boy that each must be "tamed" by the other "to establish ties," for "to me you are still nothing more than a little boy who is just like 100,000 other little boys. And I have no need of you. And you, on your part, have no need of me. To you, I am nothing more than a fox like 100,000 other foxes. But if you tame me, then we shall need each other. To me, you will be unique in all the world. To you, I shall be unique in all the world . . ."

As in the previous BIG BOOKS the stories have come from many parts of the world and have been collected by Helen Hoke Watts and Sarah Chokla Gross in New York and Ingrid Weixelbaumer in Vienna before the final selection was made in London.

London, May 1966

Margaret Green

NOTE: Occasional variations in spelling ("center" appearing as "centre," "colour" turning up as "color") mean simply that the stories printed here follow the British or American spelling and punctuation of their original translation or publication.

RASCAL

From the book of the same title

By STERLING NORTH

Sterling North, American writer, recalls a cherished pet of his boyhood, the baby raccoon he adopted when he was eleven. What follows is the opening chapter of the delightful book which Mr. North has written about this small rascal to whom he and his Saint Bernard dog, Wowser, devoted themselves.

It was in May, 1918, that a new friend and companion came into my life: a character, a personality, and a ring-tailed wonder. He weighed less than one pound when I discovered him, a furry ball of utter dependence and awakening curiosity, unweaned and defenseless. Wowser and I were immediately protective. We would have fought any boy or dog in town who sought to harm him.

Wowser was an exceptionally intelligent and responsible watchdog, guarding our house and lawns and gardens and all my pets. But because of his vast size – one hundred and seventy pounds of muscled grace and elegance – he seldom had to resort to violence.

He could shake any dog on the block as a terrier shakes a rat. Wowser never started a fight, but after being challenged, badgered, and insulted, he eventually would turn his worried face and great sad eyes upon his tormentor, and more in sorrow than in anger, grab the intruder by the scruff of the neck, and toss him into the gutter.

Wowser was an affectionate, perpetually hungry Saint Bernard. Like most dogs of his breed he drooled a little. In the house he had to lie with his muzzle on a bath towel, his eyes downcast as though in slight disgrace. Pat Delaney, a saloonkeeper who lived a couple of blocks up the street, said that Saint Bernards drool for the best of all possible reasons. He explained that in the Alps these noble dogs set forth every winter day, with little kegs of brandy strapped beneath their chins, to rescue wayfarers lost in the snowdrifts. Generations of carrying the brandy, of which they have never tasted so much as a blessed drop, have made them so thirsty that they continuously drool. The trait had now become hereditary, Pat said, and whole litters of bright and thirsty little Saint Bernards are born drooling for brandy.

On this pleasant afternoon in May, Wowser and I started up First Street toward Crescent Drive, where a semicircle of late Victorian houses enjoyed a hilltop view. Northward lay miles of meadows, groves of trees, a winding stream, and the best duck and muskrat marsh in Rock Country. As we turned down a country lane past Bardeen's orchard and vineyard, the signature of spring was everywhere: violets and anemones in the grass; the apple trees in promising bud along the bough.

Ahead lay some of the most productive walnut and hickory trees I had ever looted, a good swimming hole in the creek, and, in one bit of forest, a real curiosity – a phosphorescent stump which gleamed at night with fox-fire, as luminescent as all the lightning bugs in the world – ghostly and terrifying to boys who saw it for the first time. It scared me witless as I came home one evening from fishing. So I made it a point to bring my friends that way on other evenings, not wishing to be selfish about my pleasures.

Oscar Sunderland saw me as I passed his bleak farmhouse far down that lane. He was a friend of mine who knew enough not to talk when we went fishing. And we were trapping partners on the marsh. His mother was a gentle Norwegian woman who spoke English with no trace of an accent, and also her native language. His father Herman Sunderland was another kettle of hasenpfeffer – German on his mother's side and Swedish on his father's – with a temper and dialect all his own.

Oscar's mother baked delicious Norwegian pastries, particularly around Christmastime. Sometimes in placing before me a plate of her delicacies she would say something tender to me in Norwegian. I always turned away to hide the shameful moisture in my eyes. As Mrs. Sunderland knew, my mother had died when I was seven, and I think that was why she was especially kind to me.

Oscar's tough old father presented no such problem. I doubt that he had ever said anything kind to anyone in his life. Oscar was very much afraid of him and risked a whipping if he were not at home in time to help with the milking.

11

No one was concerned about the hours *I* kept. I was a very competent eleven-year-old. If I came home long after dark, my father would merely look up from his book to greet me vaguely and courteously. He allowed me to live my own life, keep pet skunks and woodchucks in the back yard and the barn, pamper my tame crow, my many cats, and my faithful Saint Bernard. He even let me build my eighteen-foot canoe in the living room. I had not entirely completed the framework, so it would take another year at least. When we had visitors, they sat in the easy chairs surrounding the canoe, or skirted the prow to reach the great shelves of books we were continuously lending. We lived alone and liked it, cooked and cleaned in our own fashion, and paid little attention to indignant housewives who told my father that this was no way to bring up a child.

My father agreed amiably that this might well be true, and then returned to his endless research for a novel concerning the Fox and Winnebago Indians, which for some reason was never published.

"I'm headed for Wentworth's woods," I told Oscar, "and I may not start home before moonrise."

"Wait a minute," Oscar said. "We'll need something to eat."

He returned so swiftly with a paper sack filled with coffee cake and cookies that I knew he had swiped them.

"You'll get a licking when you get home."

"Ishkabibble, I should worry!" Oscar cried, a happy grin spreading across his wide face.

We crossed the creek on the steppingstones below the dam. Pickerel were making their seasonal run up the stream, and we nearly caught one with our hands as he snaked his way between the stones. Kildeer started up from the marshy shallows, crying "kildeer, kildeer" as though a storm were brewing.

Wowser had many virtues, but he was not a hunting dog. So we were much surprised when in Wentworth's woods he came to a virtual point. Oscar and I waited silently while the Saint Bernard, on his great paws, padded softly to the hollow base of a rotten stump.

He sniffed the hole critically, then turned and whined, telling us plainly that something lived in that den.

"Dig 'em out, Wowser," I shouted.

"He won't dig," Oscar predicted. "He's too lazy."

"You just watch," I said loyally. But I wasn't betting any glass marbles.

In another minute Wowser was making the dirt fly, and Oscar and I were helping in a frenzy of excitement. We scooped the soft earth with our hands, and used our pocket knives when we came to old decaying roots.

"I'll bet it's a fox," I panted hopefully.

"Probably an old woodchuck," Oscar said.

But we couldn't have been more surprised when a furious mother raccoon exploded from her lair screaming her rage and dismay. Wowser nearly fell over backward to avoid the flying claws and slashing little teeth. A moment later the big raccoon had racked her way up a slender oak tree. Thirty feet above us she continued to scream and scold.

In plain sight now, within the den, we found four baby raccoons, a month old perhaps. The entire litter of kits might easily have fitted within my cap. Each tail had five black rings. Each small face had a sharp black mask. Eight bright eyes peered up at us, filled with wonder and worry. And from four enquiring little mouths came whimpered questions.

"Good old Wowser," I said.

"That's a pretty good dog you've got there," Oscar admitted, "but you'd better hold him back."

"He wouldn't hurt them; he takes care of all my pets."

In fact the big dog settled down with a sigh of satisfaction, as near to the nest as possible, ready to adopt one or all of these interesting little creatures. But there was one service he could not render. He could not feed them.

"We can't take them home without their mother," I told Oscar. "They're too young."

"How do we catch the mother?" Oscar asked.

"We draw straws."

"And then what?"

"The one who gets the short straw shinnies up the tree for her."

"Oh, no," Oscar said. "Oh no you don't. I ain't *that* crazy."

"Come on, Oscar."

"Nosiree."

But at just this moment the four little raccoons set up such a plaintive quavering that we all felt miserable. We *had* to catch that mother raccoon. Wowser was as sad as I was. He pointed his big muzzle toward the evening sky and howled mournfully.

"Well," Oscar said, kicking his shoe into the fresh earth, "I'd better be getting home to help with the milking."

"Quitter," I taunted.

"Who's a quitter?"

"You're a quitter."

"Well, OK, I'll draw straws; but I think you're loony."

I held the straws and Oscar drew the long one. Naturally I had to live up to my bargain. I looked far above me. In the fading glow of the sunset there she still was, twenty pounds of ring-tailed dynamite. I patted Wowser as though for the last time and began my tough scramble up that slender trunk.

As I shinnied up the tree, in no great hurry to tangle with the raccoon, I had one piece of good fortune. The full moon began to rise above an eastern hill, giving me a little more light for my dangerous maneuver. Far out on the first limb, the outraged animal took a firm stance, facing me, her eyes glowing balefully in the moonlight.

"I'm going to cut off the branch with my jackknife," I said.

"And then what?"

"You're supposed to catch her when she falls in the hazel brush."

Oscar suggested that I had bats in my belfry. But he took off his corduroy jacket and prepared to throw it over the raccoon in a do-or-die effort for which he had little enthusiasm.

Whittling through two-and-one-half inches of white oak with a fairly dull jackknife is a laborious process, as I soon discovered. I was in a cramped position, holding on with my left hand and hacking

15

away at the wood with my right. And I feared the raccoon might try to rush me when the limb began to break.

The moon rose slowly through the trees as blisters rose slowly on my right hand. But I couldn't weaken now. From far below came the whimpering of the raccoon kits, and an occasional howl from Wowser. Tree toads and frogs in the swamp began their chorus, and a little screech owl, sounding almost like another raccoon, added an eerie tremolo.

"How are you coming?" Oscar asked.

"Coming fine. Get ready to catch her."

"Count on me," Oscar said, his voice less convincing than his brave words.

The tasseled limb of the white oak sighed at last, broke with a snap, and drifted down to the hazel brush below.

Oscar tried. I will give him credit for that. He tangled for five seconds with that raccoon, and then retreated with a damaged jacket. Three of the little raccoons, hearing their mother's call, trundled with amazing swiftness into the hazel brush to follow her, and were gone. Oscar, however, was quick enough to cup one kit in his cap, our only reward for our labor – but reward enough, as time would prove. As nearly as we could tell, the handsome, sharply marked little animal was covered only with soft gray underfur, having few of the darker guard hairs which later gleam on the adult raccoon.

He was the only baby raccoon I have ever held in my hands. And as he nestled upward like a quail chick, and nuzzled like a puppy seeking his mother's milk, I was both overwhelmed with the ecstasy of ownership and frightened by the enormous responsibility we had assumed. Wowser romped beside us through the moonlight, often coming to sniff and lick the new pet we had found – this bit of masked mischief which had stolen his heart as well as my own.

"He's yours," Oscar said sadly. "My old man would never let me keep him. He shot a 'coon in the chicken house a few weeks ago."

"You can come and see him," I suggested.

"Sure, I can come and see him."

As we came up the lane toward Sunderland's farmhouse, Oscar began saying "Ishkabibble, I should worry." But he acted worried to me. When we reached his front yard he dared me and double-dared me to go up and knock on the door. Meanwhile he hid behind a flowering spirea bush and waited to see what might happen.

Oscar was wise to let me do the knocking. Herman Sunderland came storming out, swearing in German and Swedish. He was certainly angry with Oscar, and he didn't seem to like me either.

"Vere is dot no-goot son of mine?"

"It wasn't his fault," I said. "I asked him to come for a walk . . ."

"Vere iss he now?"

"Well," I said, "well . . ."

"Vell, vell, vell! Vot you mean, vell?"

"We dug out a den of raccoons," I said, "and here is the one we brought home."

"Coons!" shouted Sunderland, "verdammte varmints."

I was afraid that Mr. Sunderland might flush Oscar out, but at

just this moment Oscar's gracious mother came out on the front porch, the moonlight shining on her silvering hair.

"Go to bed, Herman," she said quietly. "I will take care of this. Come out, Oscar, from behind that bush."

To my surprise, Oscar's father meekly obeyed, taking a lamp up that long, dark parlor stairway – his shadow much taller than himself. And Oscar's mother took us to the kitchen where she fed us a warm supper and began to heat a little milk to the temperature that would be right for a human baby.

"It is hungry, the little one," she said, petting the small raccoon. "Go fetch a clean wheat straw, Oscar."

She filled her own mouth with warm milk, put the wheat straw between her lips, and slanted the straw down to the mouth of the little raccoon. I watched, fascinated, as my new pet took the straw eagerly and began to nurse.

"Look how the little one eats," Oscar's mother said. "This is the way you will have to feed him, Sterling."

PETER'S PET GOATS

From the book "Heidi"

BY JOHANNA SPYRI

This little Swiss girl has been loved by children all over the world for eighty years. Her life in the mountain village with her grandfather and the goatherd, Peter, starts when she is ten. In this story she is climbing up to the mountain pasture for the very first time.

Peter and Heidi went off merrily, climbing up the mountain. The last traces of clouds were swept from the sky, and it was now a wonderful deep blue. The mountain was covered with blue and yellow flowers. Their wide-open flower faces seemed to be laughing back at the sun, while everything shimmered and shone in the bright clear air.

Heidi scampered this way and that, shouting for joy. Here it was a whole field of red primroses; there the place was blue with gentians. All around, tender yellow buttercups nodded in the sunlight. Beckoned everywhere by new and delightful sights, Heidi forgot the goats and even Peter as she gathered great handfuls of flowers and stuffed them into her apron. She intended to carry them home with her and put them in the hay in her loft, to make her room look like the flower-strewn Alm.

Poor Peter felt as if his eyes had to see everywhere. His round eyes were not used to moving very quickly and he surely had enough to do that day. For the goats, like Heidi, ran in all directions while Peter whistled and shouted and swung his rod to bring them together again and again.

Heidi's apron was so full that there was not room for another flower. Now she kept pace with Peter; and the goats, too, went in better order, for they smelled the sweet herbs in their pasture on the heights and pushed forward steadily. The pasture where Peter usually spent the day was at the foot of the peak. The base, covered with scrub pines and bushes, rose steeply toward the sky. On one side of the Alm there were deep chasms, and the old man had been right to warn the children of that danger.

Having reached the highest point, Peter took of his knapsack and placed it carefully in a small hollow where it would be safe from the gusty mountain wind. Peter knew that wind very well, and he did not mean to see his knapsack and his nice dinner go rolling down the hillside. After making sure of its safety, Peter stretched himself on the sunny ground, to rest after the steep climb.

Suddenly Peter began to whistle and to call so loudly that Heidi did know what was happening. But the goats knew, and all came running and leaping, and were soon gathered on the green pasture. Some nibbled at the grass, others ran about, and a pair stood opposite each other and butted playfully with their horns.

Heidi ran in among the gamboling goats, and dashed from one to another to make herself acquainted with each separately. Each had its own charm for her; each one looked and behaved differently.

While Heidi played with the goats, Peter brought out the knapsack, and arranged the food in a square on the grass. The large pieces of bread and cheese he put on Heidi's side, the small ones on his own. Then, filling the mug with fresh milk from Schwänli, he placed it in the center of the square.

With his grass table set, Peter called Heidi, but the child was so absorbed in the pranks of her new playfellows, that she heard nothing. Now Peter shouted so loud that he could have been heard up on the topmost rocks, and this time Heidi ran to him as fast as she could. Seeing the inviting table, she clapped her hands.

"Stop jumping about and eat," said Peter crossly, sitting down.

"Is the milk for me?" Heidi asked.

"Yes, and the big chunks of bread and cheese are yours also. When you finish the milk, you may have another mug full from Schwänli. After you finish yours, it will be my turn."

"Where do you get your milk?" the little girl asked curiously.

"From my goat, Snail. Eat now. Go ahead."

Heidi began with the milk, and when she had emptied the mug,

Peter rose and filled it again. She broke some of her bread into the milk, and then held out the rest of it toward Peter. It was a big piece, still twice as large as his, which he had already eaten, together with his cheese. Heidi looked at her cheese and then gave it to him also, the whole big lump, saying: "Take it, I've had enough."

Peter stared at Heidi, speechless. Never in his whole life had he been able to give such food away. He hesitated, for he could not believe that Heidi was in earnest, but the child smiled and nodded and at last laid the food on his knee.

Convinced that she was serious, he took the gift, bobbed his head in thanks and pleasure, and made of it the heartiest meal he'd had since he first tended the goats. While he feasted, Heidi watched the flock.

"What are the goats' names?" she asked Peter.

He knew them all, of course, and rattled the names off without hesitation, pointing each one out as he spoke. Heidi gave him her entire attention, and soon could name them all herself.

23

There was big Turk with powerful horns, who always butted the others, so that they scampered away whenever he drew near them. They would have nothing to do with this roughneck. Only the brave, slender Thistlebird did not run away, but struck out sharply, once, twice, six times, until the great Turk stood still in astonishment and made no further trouble. Thistlebird had sharp horns, too, and knew how to use them.

Little white Snowball, who always bleated beseechingly, often had Heidi running to take its head between her hands to comfort it. Now the child ran to it again, for she heard the wailing cry, and she put her arm around the small creature's neck saying: "What is wrong, Snowball? Why do you cry like this?"

The animal pressed close to the little girl, and was quiet.

Peter explained Snowball's trouble. "She cries because her old one does not come with us any more. She was sold to Mayenfeld, day before yesterday, and will not come to the Alm any more."

"Who is the old one?" Heidi asked.

"Its mother," Peter answered.

"Where is the grandmother?" Heidi wanted to know.

"She has none," Peter shrugged.

"And the grandfather?"

"None."

"Oh. Poor little Snowball!" Heidi moaned tenderly, pressing the goat close to her side. "Don't cry any more. I'll come here every day, then you won't be lonely. And when you feel sad, come to me."

Snowball rubbed her head against Heidi and bleated no more.

When Peter finished his ample dinner, he rose to look after his flock again. The goats had already begun to wander.

The loveliest and cleanest of the goats were Schwänli and Bärli. They behaved better than the others, and usually went their own way. They avoided the disagreeable Turk particularly.

The animals had begun to climb up again toward the bushes, springing lightly over every obstacle, Turk trying to give someone a blow whenever he could. Schwänli and Bärli climbed prettily, in a delicate and dainty manner. Heidi put her hands behind her back, and watched them as they went higher and higher.

Peter had thrown himself down on the ground again, and turning to him, Heidi said, "The prettiest of all are Schwänli and Bärli."

"Of course," Peter replied. "The Alm-Uncle brushes and combs them and gives them salt daily along with nice clean stalls."

All at once the lad sprang to his feet and was off after the goats with great leaps, and instantly Heidi was after him, for surely something must have happened, and she could not stay behind.

Peter raced through the flock toward the side of the Alm, where the rocks rose up steep and bare, and where a careless goat might easily fall, and get all its legs broken. He had noticed that the bold Thistlebird had strayed in that direction, and came after her barely in time, for she had reached the very edge of a precipice. He was about to seize her, when he tripped and fell, grasping her only by the leg as he came down hard on the ground. He didn't let go, but held her fast, though she bleated with surprise and annoyance to find herself so held.

The goatherd called loudly to Heidi, for he was unable to get to his feet and it seemed to him that he was pulling the little goat's leg off, she was so determined to go on. Heidi ran to him.

Seeing the danger of the situation to him and to the goat, she pulled up a sweet-smelling herb and thrust it under Thistlebird's nose, soothing the creature with "Come, little goat, be good, Thistlebird. See now, you might have fallen and broken your bones and that would have hurt you, indeed."

25

The goat turned to nibble at the herb held out by Heidi. Peter scrambled to his feet, and hurriedly seized the rope that hung from Thistlebird's collar, while Heidi grabbed the collar from the other side. Together they led her between them to the rest of the flock, peacefully grazing below.

With his goat safe once more, Peter raised his rod and was about to whip her soundly. Thistlebird drew back, alarmed, for she saw what was coming.

Heidi saw it, too, and screamed out in terror, "No, Peter, no! Don't hit her! See how frightened she is!"

"She deserves to be punished," Peter said angrily, and raised the rod again; but the child seized his arm, and held it.

"You must let her alone!" she cried.

Peter stared amazed by her commanding tone and flashing eyes. His arm dropped to his side. "Very well, she may go, but you will have to give me some of your cheese tomorrow." He felt that he must have some reward for the fright the silly goat had given him.

"You shall have it all, tomorrow and every day. I do not want it," said Heidi. "You may have a big piece of bread also, as big as I gave today. But you must promise me not to hit Thistlebird or Snowball, or any of the goats."

Peter shrugged. "It's all the same to me," he said, and for him that was a promise. He let the culprit go, and the happy goat leaped back in among the others.

THE CHRISTMAS PONY

From the book "Boy on Horseback"

By LINCOLN STEFFENS

Lincoln Steffens, renowned in America after the turn of the century as a
"muck-raking" journalist, an exposer of political corruption, a crusader,
grew from the California lad who had the enduring satisfaction of
owning a horse. The full story of how important the horse was to the boy,
and of the high-principled father (who cuts a poor figure in the following incident) is told in *The Autobiography of Lincoln Steffens.*

What interested me in our new neighborhood was not the
school, nor the room I was to have in the new house all to myself,
but the stable which was built back of the house. My father let me
direct the making of a stall, a little smaller than the other stalls, for
my pony, and I prayed and hoped and my sister Lou believed that
that meant that I would get the pony, perhaps for Christmas. I
pointed out to her that there were three other stalls and no horses
at all. This I said in order that she should answer it. She could not.
My father, sounded out, said that some day we might have horses
and a cow; meanwhile a stable added to the value of a house. "Some
day" is a pain to a boy who lives in and knows only "now". My good
little sisters, to comfort me, remarked that Christmas was coming,
but Christmas was always coming and grown-ups were always talking about it, asking you what you wanted and then giving you
what they wanted you to have.

Though everybody knew what I wanted, I told them all again.
My mother knew that I told God, too, every night. I wanted a pony,
and to make sure they understood, I declared that I wanted nothing
else.

"Nothing but a pony?" my father asked.

"Nothing," I said.

"Not even a pair of high boots?"

That was hard. I did want boots, but I stuck to the pony. "No,
not even boots."

27

"Nor candy? There ought to be something to fill your stocking with, and Santa Claus can't put a pony into a stocking."

That was true, and he couldn't lead a pony down the chimney either. But no. "All I want is a pony," I said. "If I can't have a pony, give me nothing, nothing."

Now I had been looking myself for the pony I wanted, going to sales stables, inquiring of horsemen, and I had seen several that would do. My father let me "try" them. I tried so many ponies that I was learning fast to sit a horse. I chose several, but my father always found some fault with them. I was in despair. When Christmas was at hand I had given up all hope of a pony, and on Christmas Eve I hung up my stocking along with my sisters', of whom, by the way, I now had three.

I haven't mentioned my sisters or their coming because, you understand, they were girls, and girls, young girls, counted for nothing in my manly life. They did not mind me either; they were so happy that Christmas Eve that I caught some of their merriment. I speculated on what I'd get. I hung up the biggest stocking I had, and we all went reluctantly to bed to wait until morning. Not to sleep; not right away. We were told that we must not only sleep promptly, we must not wake up until seven-thirty – if we did, we must not go the fireplace for our Christmas. Impossible.

We did sleep that night, but we woke up at six a. m. We lay in our beds and debated through the open doors whether to obey until, say, half-past six. Then we bolted. I don't know who started it, but there was a rush. We all disobeyed; we raced to disobey and get first to the fireplace in the front room downstairs. And there they were, the gifts, all sorts of wonderful things, mixed-up piles of presents; only, as I disentangled the mess, I saw that my stocking was empty; it hung limp; not a thing in it; and under and around it – nothing. My sisters had knelt down, each by her pile of gifts; they were squealing with delight, until they looked up and saw me standing there in my nightgown with nothing.

28

They left their piles to come to me and look with me at my empty place. Nothing. They felt my stocking: nothing.

I don't remember whether I cried at that moment, but my sisters did. They ran with me back to my bed, and there we all cried until I became indignant. That helped some. I got up, dressed, and driving my sisters away, I went alone out into the yard, down to the stable, and there, all by myself, I wept. My mother came out to me by and by; she found me in my pony stall, sobbing on the floor, and she tried to comfort me. But I heard my father outside; he had come part way with her, and she was having some sort of angry quarrel with him. She tried to comfort me; besought me to come to breakfast. I could not; I wanted no comfort and no breakfast. She left me and went on into the house with sharp words for my father.

I don't know what kind of breakfast the family had. My sisters said it was "awful". They were ashamed to enjoy their own toys. They came to me, and I was rude. I ran away from them. I went around to the front of the house, sat down on the steps, and, the crying over, I ached. I was wronged, I was hurt – I can feel now what I felt then, and I am sure that if one could see the wounds upon our hearts, there would be found still upon mine a scar from that terrible Christmas morning. And my father, the practical joker, he must have been hurt, too, a little. I saw him looking out of the window. He was watching me or something for an hour or two, drawing back the curtain ever so little lest I catch him, but I saw his face, and I think I can see now the anxiety upon it, the worried impatience.

After, I don't know how long, surely an hour or two, I was brought to the climax of my agony by the sight of a man riding a pony down the street, a pony and a brand-new saddle; the most beautiful saddle I ever saw, and it was a boy's saddle; the man's feet were not in the stirrups; his legs were too long. The outfit was perfect; it was the realization of all my dreams, the answer to all my prayers. A fine new bridle, with a light curb bit. And the pony! As he

drew near, I saw that the pony was really a small horse – what we called an Indian pony, a bay, with black mane and tail, and one white foot and a white star on his forehead. For such a horse as that I would have given, I could have given, anything.

But the man, a disheveled fellow with a blackened eye and a fresh-cut face, came along, reading the numbers on the houses, and, as my hopes – my impossible hopes – rose, he looked at our door and passed by, he and the pony, and the saddle and the bridle. Too much. I fell upon the steps, and having wept before, I broke now into such a flood of tears that I was a floating wreck when I heard a voice.

"Say, kid," it said, "do you know a boy named Lennie Steffens?"

I looked up. It was the man on the pony, back again, at our horse block.

"Yes," I spluttered through my tears, "That's me."

"Well," he said, "then this is your horse. I've been looking all over for you and your house. Why don't you put your number where it can be seen?"

"Get down," I said, running out to him.

He went on saying something about "ought to have got here at seven o'clock; told me to bring the nag here and tie him to your post and leave him for you. But I got into a drunk – and a fight – and a hospital – and –"

"Get down," I said.

He got down, and he boosted me up to the saddle. He offered to fit the stirrups to me, but I didn't want him to. I wanted to ride.

"What's the matter with you?" he said, angrily. "What you crying for? Don't you like the horse? He's a dandy, this horse. I know him of old. He's fine at cattle; he'll drive 'em alone."

I hardly heard, I could scarcely wait, but he persisted. He adjusted the stirrups, and then, finally, off I rode, slowly, at a walk, so happy, so thrilled, that I did not know what I was doing. I did not look back at the house or the man, I rode off up the street, taking note of everything – of the reins, of the pony's long mane, of the carved leather saddle. I had never known anything so beautiful. And mine! I was going to ride up past Miss Kay's house. But I noticed on the horn of the saddle some stains like rain-drops, so I turned and trotted home, not to the house but to the stable. There was the family, father, mother, sisters, all working for me, all happy. They had been putting in place the tools of my new business: blankets, currycomb, brush, pitchfork – everything, and there was hay in the loft.

"What did you come back so soon for?" somebody asked. "Why didn't you go on riding?"

I pointed to the stains. "I wasn't going to get my new saddle rained on," I said. And my father laughed. "It isn't raining," he said. "Those are not rain-drops."

"They are tears," my mother gasped, and she gave my father a look which sent him off to the house. Worse still, my mother offered to wipe away the tears still running out of my eyes. I gave her such a look as she had given him, and she went off after my father, drying her own tears. My sisters remained and we all unsaddled the pony, put on his halter, led him to his stall, tied and fed him. It began really to rain; so all the rest of that memorable day we curried and combed that pony. The girls plaited his mane, forelock, and tail, while I pitchforked hay to him and curried and brushed, curried and brushed. For a change we brought him out to drink; we led him up and down, blanketed like a race-horse; we took turns at that. But the best, the most inexhaustible fun, was to clean him. When we went reluctantly to our midday Christmas dinner, we all smelt of horse, and my sisters had to wash their faces and hands. I was asked to, but I wouldn't until my mother bade me look in the mirror. Then I washed up – quick. My face was caked with the muddy lines of tears that had coursed over my cheeks to my mouth. Having washed away that shame, I ate my dinner, and as I ate I grew hungrier and hungrier. It was my first meal that day, and as I filled up on the turkey and the stuffing, the cranberries and the pies, the fruit and the nuts – as I swelled, I could laugh. My mother said I still choked and sobbed now and then, but I laughed, too; I saw and enjoyed my sisters' presents until – I had to go out and attend to my pony, who was there, really and truly there, the promise, the beginning of a happy double life. And – I went and looked to make sure – there was the saddle, too, and the bridle.

But that Christmas, which my father had planned so carefully, was it the best or the worst I ever knew? He often asked me that; I never could answer as a boy. I think now that it was both. It covered the whole distance from broken-hearted misery to bursting happiness – too fast. A grown-up could hardly have stood it.

GRISHKA'S BEAR

From the book "Grishka and the Bear"

By RENÉ GUILLOT

Grishka was one of the people of Murkvo, in northern Siberia, hunters
of the black bear. Secretly following the men on a hunt, young Grishka
brought back the little cub of the great mother bear just killed. For a
year, as the tribesmen pampered little Djidi, the bear grew and Grishka
played and hunted with his beloved "little brother". Looming ever closer,
though, was the day when, by tribal law, the unwitting and trustful Djidi
must be sacrificed at the festival of the bear. The chief would give a
sign to a Murkvo warrior whose spear would strike death to Djidi. Grishka
knew that he must defy the ancient law or see his dear bear friend killed.
Like his father Orsok, who had defied the village and left, the boy made his
choice. One dark night, Grishka took Djidi away from the ceremonial tent.

None but the trees had been there to hear what the boy was saying
to the bear he was leading back to his mountain home. "We're going
to live with the bears, little brother, and we'll always be together."

Ever since he had left the village, Grishka had been living up
among the bears, accepted as one of their clan. It was their turn
now to adopt a cub not of their own kind, as the village had done,
and they had soon grown accustomed to having him in their midst.
Djidi, his enormous "little brother", watched over him. They shared
the same bed of straw and bracken in the depths of the caves.
Together they went searching for berries and the black bees' honey,
and Grishka set traps for birds.

The boy had always dreamed of a wonderful life like this. The
whole wide forest was his domain. He had no regrets about leaving
the village of Murkvo which had driven out his father. Grishka
could be justly proud of being Orsok's son. Like him he had,
young as he was, the remarkably sure instincts of the true hunter.

Only this time it was he who was being hunted. And Grishka
had no way of knowing that his father finally had returned and
followed to take him home.

He saw the men crossing the slopes and starting to climb the red mountains. "They want to capture you again, little brother. But we'll give them the slip. I'll stand by you."

Grishka knew when the hunters made a halt. And he knew exactly where: over by the clearing where the bilberries and myrtles grew. Grishka watched from above, for the men were just below the caves where the bears had their winter quarter.

The boy fled from his pursuers, and with him went Djidi and the whole family of bears. He got well ahead, for he did not see them again for two days. "I wonder why they haven't brought dogs," Grishka said to himself, as he fled down the farther slopes.

Then the men appeared again. They had gone round the main range and were approaching from the other side.

From their first catching the men's scent, the bears were frightened. They kept growling and stopping to listen to the mountain echoes, nervous at the slightest sound. At last, impelled by instinct to save themselves, they went off and left the boy and his black prince in the middle of the wood. Grishka and Djidi were alone again.

"They're scared, little brother. But I'm more cunning than they."

Grishka got up from where he had been crouching with his ear to the rocks and came across to Djidi. "The men are still a long way off. They must have lost track of us. They'll never catch us. The rest of your family will have to chance their luck alone, Djidi. Well, so much the worse for them."

The bear grunted.

"I can see I shall have to take your whistle away. No, Djidi . . . No."

Djidi let go of the little metal toy he loved, which sang as if birds were shut inside it, and let it fall back on to his furry chest.

"Come along; we'd better get on." To throw his pursuers off the scent once and for all, Grishka decided to make for the small, shallow mountain stream. When he reached it he would step into the clear water and walk along the pebbly bed upstream with Djidi. They would not look for him that way, and he and Djidi would be safe once they reached the high peaks.

Retracing his steps so as to cut through the clearer part of the wood, Grishka never suspected that his luck had turned against him and that he would never reach the stream.

Djidi let out a growl. Stop . . . Was it the men already or some wild animal?

"Quiet, Djidi."

The animal trampled the ground.

"Come on."

How dense the darkness was among the close-growing tree trunks in this oppressive wood! And how still – disturbingly still. The forest was listening.

All hunters know that dizziness that seizes you, the anguish that suddenly clutches your heart when fear strikes the *taïga*. Just the rustle of a leaf, the snap of a twig, and you are on the *qui vive*. Your knees turn to jelly. You are rooted to the spot and have one idea only: to run as fast as you can.

Djidi kept trampling the ferns and growling to himself.

Boy and bear fell a prey to fear.

41

The whole forest was silent.

A hundred yards away where the dark, oppressive wood ended, Grishka could see the wide clearing full of light. He rushed forward. Despite his exhaustion after two days and two nights on the run, his legs were agile under the impulse of fear. They seemed to lose their stiffness and carry him swiftly so that Djidi found it hard to keep up with him.

Grishka was already a good way ahead when suddenly the ground seemed to give way. He did not even have time to cry out. With a cracking of dead branches, the solid forest floor of dry grass and ferns gave way beneath his feet and in he fell, into an old pit which had been dug by hunters some time or another for a trap. The hole had been camouflaged with interlaced branches which fell in when he stepped on them.

From some way off Djidi saw his friend disappear into the ground. He came running up and stopped at the edge where he crouched down and looked in. There was not a sound – not so much as the rustle of a leaf. Djidi stayed there trembling and listened intently, with turmoil in his heart. Silence. No sound came from the pit.

Then the distracted animal began to go around and around, beating his chest and growling and spitting with rage. Every now and again he would stop and trample the ground until more crumbled and fell into the hole. Then the poor creature would start going around again, quite lost and helpless.

Twenty times he crouched down and looked into the dark depths where his friend was lying.

Grishka had fainted from the shock of the fall. He could hear the bear calling him plaintively with little strangled cries, his teeth chattering with fear. Luckily, the men were still a long way away.

Perhaps it was some instinct inherited from the bears that showed Djidi a way to try to save his friend. All animals have ingenious tricks which they have learned in the course of being hunted by men. Who knows – more than one mother bear may have saved

42

the cub this way. And if Grishka had not been stunned in his fall, if he had remained conscious, he too could have been saved.

Djidi ran across to the trees, climbed up one of the thick trunks and settled himself in a fork. And there he pushed with all his might until a thick bough snapped. He climbed down, took hold of it, and dragged it off to the hole. He grunted down into it. Was his friend never going to answer him?

Again he grunted. He thrust the great bough down into the hole so that Grishka could climb out by holding on to its branches. Djidi had done everything he could to save his friend, but still there was no movement down there in the pit.

Then the bear felt deserted, utterly abandoned. Panic seized him

and he ran wildly to and fro and at last, like his brothers, rushed away as if he neither knew nor cared where he was going. One would have thought him mad at that moment; he did not even seem to smell the man-smell coming closer. He was running straight into the arms of the hunters . . .

But Djidi, who loved the boy, was not running away. Nor was it fear that stopped him doing so.

The first person to see him was Orsok. "Don't shoot," he said, for Vanya, beside him, was drawing his bow.

In any case, the bear had stopped some distance away, beyond the range of an arrow and seemed to be waiting.

"It's Grishka's bear," murmured old Kia. "Look, Orsok." What was the animal doing? Half hidden behind a tree, he seemed to be fumbling for something on his chest; then he lifted his paw to his mouth, and they heard a shrill note. He was blowing on the whistle just as he used to when he wanted to attract Grishka's attention.

"We'll go on, very quietly," said Orsok.

The bear, still out of range, had not moved. And yet, it must have seen the men. The hunters went on towards it, taking no cover.

"Gently . . . and don't shoot," said Orsok again. They were near enough to throw their spears. But then they saw the bear move back, watching them all the time. It did not go straight back but around the bushes, following the line of red rocks until it plunged in among the trees.

An arrow whistled through the air. "Vanya," shouted Orsok, "didn't I forbid you to shoot?" He seized the man's bow and broke it over his knees. But the arrow had struck Djidi in the haunch. The bear fell back onto all fours. With a savage snap, he pulled out the broken arrow. But instead of running away, he still kept moving back towards the clearing – where the pit was. The wounded animal drew the men after it all the way and led the hunters to the trap in which his friend Grishka was lying.

Orsok, ahead of the rest, saw the hole and noticed the big branch that Djidi had thrust down into it. He saw Grishka's rifle lying in the trampled grass, for the boy had dropped it as he fell.

45

"Quickly . . . give me a hand," he cried. The men came hurrying.

"It's an old pit," said Kia.

"But deep enough. The boy may have broken his leg," said a voice. "I'll go down to him."

"No, I will," said Orsok, and he caught hold of the branch and let himself down by it.

The bear squatted down a hundred paces away and began licking the blood from his wound. Everything was mixed up for Djidi in his animal brain. Were these not men from Murkvo? They must know him, for he had lived with them in their own village. And yet they had shot him. The iron head of the arrow was so deeply in that he had to tear the flesh to pull it out.

The men were watching at a distance as if they were frightened of him – frightened of Grishka's Djidi! He was in pain and growled softly. Instinctively, from long habit, Djidi's trembling paw went up to his neck and groped feverishly for his whistle. Then he let out a long howl: the whistle was gone! The chain must have come undone, and he had lost Grishka's whistle.

It was a dismal cry. Some of the men looked around, shivering in the chill air. Suddenly the bear straightened and grunted, with joy as well as fear in his eyes. Although he was hurt and suffering, he was happy, too, for he saw a man pull himself out of the hole – Orsok, with the unconscious Grishka hanging limply over his shoulder.

The bear came a step nearer. It was Grishka – his beloved little brother. He longed to run to him, but his legs were trembling. All he wanted was to be beside his friend, but fear gripped him still and would never leave him, now that the men had struck him and destroyed his trust.

There lay Grishka with the men all around him, bending over him. Djidi took another step forward, stood hesitating a moment, then stepped back again.

The men had taken Grishka from him. All at once, as if it were an actual hunt and he had been chased, he seemed to realize at last (it had taken Grishka so long to teach him that he was really a bear), and he turned and limped slowly away.

"The bear's going," said old Kia.

But Orsok did not look up; his one thought was to bring his son back to consciousness. The colour was coming back slowly into the boy's cheeks.

"There's nothing broken," said Orsok, feeling over his whole body long and carefully. "Ah, he's opening his eyes."

Two or three times the bear stopped, his outline almost indistinguishable now against the dark trees, and looked back at the group of hunters. He was limping, and his wound was hurting.

Why had the men wanted to hurt him?

Djidi stopped suddenly; he thought he heard Grishka's bright laugh, that wonderful gurgling sound like the song of a fountain that had always fascinated him. No. The wood was silent. It drew back timidly, its lines of trees stealing away into their own shadows; and the wood took Djidi with it, back to where he belonged.

Grishka, lying on the grass, beside the hole, gradually came to. He could not remember what had happened.

He did not know that Orsok and his men had just pulled him out of a bear trap.

Nor did he know that it was his friend Djidi, with an arrow in his haunch, who had led the men to the hole to rescue him. Djidi, to save Grishka's life, had sacrificed the friendship that meant everything to him. He was walking on deeper into the mountains, dazed and distracted, quite unable to understand the malevolence of the men who had hunted him.

Grishka's lips moved; old Kia, kneeling beside him, leaned forward and tried to catch what he was saying. "I think he's been more frightened than hurt," said the chief. "He's opening his eyes; he's trying to speak." They could not catch what he was trying to say, he was still so weak. Orsok came very close and put his ear to the trembling lips. All he could hear was a stammered:

"Djidi . . . Djidi . . . Where's Djidi? Where's my little brother?"

RICOTTE

From the book "Creatures Great and Small"

By COLETTE

This great French writer made pets of all kinds of animals during her long life (1873 — 1954). In this book she describes some of them. The stranger ones included lizards, grasshoppers, goldfish, a pair of snakes, a robin, a blue parakeet, and of course the squirrel, Ricotte. But most beloved were the dogs — the brindled French bulldogs, Toby-dog and Poucette, the yellow collie, the sly-eyed schipperke, the sheepdog, Vorace, and the terriers; and the cats — Angora tabby, Kiki-the-Demure, the black cat, Poun, the alley cat, Perrou, the old Persian and the young Persian, She-Shah, among many others.

The she-cats, hair on end, leapt in the air like swift and terrible birds. "A rat! A rat!" they cried.

But it was not a rat. It was merely a female Brazilian squirrel, a little squirrel who at first meeting showed them her sharp claws, and two front teeth sharp enough to cut glass.

"It obviously isn't a rat," said the mother Cat. "I must have time to think."

"I must think too," repeated the daughter Cat obediently. She was the living image of her mother, and not exactly the inventor of the mouse-trap.

Meanwhile the squirrel was drinking the milk put out to welcome her, holding the edge of the bowl with both hands. Then she wiped her little nose on the velvet of the armchair, combed herself with her ten fingers, like a romantic poet, scratched one ear, arranged her tail like a question-mark up her back, and cracked herself some hazelnuts.

49

Next the bitch came up, thoroughly disgusted, to sniff the new creature; but the squirrel coughed fretfully at her, going "huh! huh!" like a testy professor, and the bitch, not having thought out a plan of campaign, made off. The new creature remained alone before us and began to act according to the code of the genuine wild animal who, suddenly confronted with a well-meaning Two-Footed One, tackles him in some such terms as: "You are not an enemy of mine? Then you must be my friend. So once and for all I put my whole trust in you." With that she sprang onto my shoulder and gave me her biggest nut to keep, pushing it well down between my neck and the collar of my blouse, and pulling out a lock of my hair to cover it.

The next day I severed her chain. How could one keep that elfin sprite, that flying spark, on a chain? Or chain up that exile who had crossed the seas in a cage and taken me for her new fatherland? She felt her bonds break, but dared not believe it, and remained for a moment quivering and sitting like a kangaroo, her two forepaws clasped against her chest as though overcome with emotion. Then, almost awkwardly, she risked first one small, incredulous leap, then another longer one which landed her, light as thistledown, on the sill of the open window. But after that she gave a third jump, more assured than the first two, and this one brought her onto my shoulder.

And in that arc-like leap of hers through the air she crossed the mystic bridge over the gulf that separates the souls of beasts from our souls.

There she is, in front of me. The minute before she was elsewhere, and the minute after where will she be? I have known her such a short time that I have difficulty, every morning, in recalling her shape and colour; so each time I wake she astonishes me afresh. A black stripe, like that on a mule's back, runs down the length of hers; her flanks, covered with short, smooth fur, are almost bronze-green and a splendid foil for the warm red of her belly and the plume of a tail that matches it, a glowing, red plume of fine, smooth hairs, which makes you say when you first see it: "Why is Ricotte wearing an ostrich feather on her behind?"

As for her eyes, they are squirrel's eyes, which is as much as to say that they are beautiful, wide-open and bright. Her ears are rounded like the ears of mice and neatly finished at the edges with a ridge like a little rolled hem. And though one of her little monkey hands is enough to cause the most artful destruction, she is extravagantly furnished with four of them!

51

There she is now, crossing the table, leaping on her hind paws because her front ones are carefully clasping a huge wad of absorbent cotton wool which she has stolen. Every day Ricotte appropriates some new chattel. Thanks to her, a ball of string turns back into hanks of hemp, and the telephone flex into hanks of silk. She has made her nest in the middle of a large bundle of wool, and there she sleeps and washes, shreds almonds and comments on passing events with her reproachful "huh! huh!"

Back she comes with empty paws and sits down to keep me company. The trouble is that when she looks at me I cannot help laughing, and she replies with her own squirrel-gaiety, expressed in a lightning somersault so swift that afterwards one wonders whether one has seen it.

Yesterday the full sugar-basin upset her because she despaired of finding in the room a hiding-place for each piece of sugar. This morning she is comforted: having put the stolen pieces back in their place, one by one, she mounts guard beside the basin. I find almonds in my overboots and bits of biscuit inserted like sachets among my underclothes. There are candle-ends in my powder box and... and, dear me, whatever's that crackling under the carpet? Pastilles of chlorate of potassium! Ricotte's treating her throat. And we must not feel surprised if burglars get into our house in the night, because Ricotte has filled the slots of all the bolts with walnuts.

KATE'S FROGGERY

From the book "My Garden of Memory"

By KATE DOUGLAS WIGGIN

Known to millions of readers for her *Rebecca of Sunnybrook Farm* (1903),
Kate Douglas Wiggin was a kindergarten teacher before she became a
writer. It was to support the kindergarten that she turned to writing, and
with her *The Birds' Christmas Carol* she won a wide public. But before she
was old enough to think of directing a kindergarten, Kate and her little sister Nora played at directing a frogs' chorus, as she recalls in the last book
of her life.

In the spring we searched for mayflowers, and waded in the full
brooks and gathered fluffy pussy willows. There were anemones and
frail hepaticas in the woods and blue flags and wild violets in the
marshy places. We watched the yellow dandelions come, one by
one, in the short green grass, and we stood under the maple trees
and saw the sap trickle from their trunks into the great wooden
buckets placed underneath.

If spring seemed wonderful, summer was even more joyous, with
strawberrying and blueberrying and haymaking; – long days of
play and long twilights and moonlight nights.

One of our pleasures was a little out of the ordinary: I asked my
stepfather one day if he would give us a part of the garden brook for
our "froggery". The garden in question covered an acre or two of
ground, with little up-hills and down-dales, while a dashing, tu-
multuous brook, with here and there a bit of quiet water, ran through
it. There were many trees, with flower-beds bordering the road, and
there was a green-and-white latticed summer-house on the brink
of the hill at the foot of which flowed our beloved Saco River.
In one of the deep, quiet pools of the brook, hidden by green alder
bushes, my father put pieces of fine wire netting, and so arranged
them that the frogs we caught and placed there lived a pleasant and
secluded life free from the cares and dangers that we fancied existed
in large ponds.

Here we used to wait for gay young polliwogs to grow into frogs, one leg at a time. Repeated and prolonged observations by the pond never once permitted us to see a leg actually coming out. Nature somehow decreed that it should happen in the night.

We found two wounded bullfrogs by the side of the waterlily pond, magnificent bass singers, stoned by cruel small boys. We bound up their broken legs and bruised backs and coaxed them into health again in one corner of the froggery that we called the hospital. In another corner was the nursery, kept only for the tiniest frogs; but with a dawning pedagogical instinct we let them out once a day so that they might not be cut off from the advantages of adult society. All our frogs had names of their own and we knew them all apart. They always had plenty of fat juicy flies and waterbugs for dinner, and sometimes we put little silver shiners and tiny minnows into the pool. "They will know now, you see, that there are other things in the world except frogs," I explained to the Small Sister, who did not favor the idea, principally because she could never lean over the fishy part of the brook to catch minnows without tumbling in head foremost.

We held a frog singing-school once a week. It was very trouble-some, but exciting. We used to put a nice little board across the pool and then catch the frogs and try to keep them in line with their heads all facing the same way during the brief lesson. They never really caught the idea, and were never in a singing mood until just before our own early bedtime, when the baby frogs were so sleepy that they kept falling from the board into the pool. They could never quite apprehend the difference between school and pool; but at the end of the summer's training we twice succeeded in getting them into line, quiet, docile, motionless, without a hint of the application of force; tact, moral suasion, and superhuman patience being the only means employed.

It was a beautiful sight worth any amount of toil and trouble! Twenty-one frogs in line, for a minute and a half, all graded nicely as to size, all in fresh green suits with white shirt-fronts. What wonder that in various sojourns in Paris I have never been able to regard a frog's leg as an appetizing delicacy, or to hear its resemblance and superiority to chicken discussed without a shudder. As soon dine upon the breast of the family kitten!

MISS NIGHTINGALE'S PETS

From the book "Florence Nightingale"

By CECIL WOODHAM-SMITH

The great Victorian nurse went on many strange journeys. Here she is crossing the desert, in unusual company.

She found relief in the companionship of animals. On the Nile she had two little chamelions which slept on her bed and she had been "so sorry to part with them, they were such company". She was travelling now with two tortoises – called Mr. and Mrs. Hill in honour of two missionaries at Athens – a cicada named Plato, and Athena, a baby owl, which she had rescued from some Greek boys at the Parthenon. Athena was fierce, and Miss Nightingale had had to mesmerize her according to Richard Monckton Milne's method, before she could be persuaded to enter a cage, but she became devoted to her mistress and travelled everywhere in her pocket.

At Prague Athena ate Plato.

ELSA GOES TO THE INDIAN OCEAN

From the book "Born Free"

By JOY ADAMSON

This lioness, Elsa, who became such a wonderful friend to Joy Adamson without ever losing her freedom and ability to live her natural life in the East African bush, must be one of the most famous of all pets. Her career was followed by people interested in animals all over the world. Here she first meets the sea.

Our local leave was due and we planned to spend it by the sea, on a remote part of the coast, close to a small Barjun fishing village and not far from the Somali border. The nearest white population was ninety miles south in Lamu. It would be a perfect for place Elsa, for we could camp on the beach, away from people, with miles of clean sand around us, and a bushy hinterland behind would provide shade.

As soon as the sun was up the whole camp trooped down to the water's edge to introduce her to the Indian Ocean. The tide was receding; at first she was nervous of the unaccustomed roar and rush of the waves. Then she sniffed cautiously at the water, bit at the foam; finally, she put her head down to drink, but her first mouthful of salt water made her wrinkle her nose and pull grimaces of disgust. However, when she saw the rest of the party enjoying a swim, she decided to trust us and join in the fun. Very soon she became quite water-crazy. Rain pools and shallow rivers had always excited and invigorated her, but this great ocean was a real heaven for her. She swam effortlessly, far out of her depth; ducked us and splashed the water with her tail.

She followed us everywhere, so I usually stayed behind when the others went fishing; otherwise she would have swum out after our boat.

She loved walking along the beach, where she chased the coconuts bobbing in the surf, getting splashed and swamped by the waves

61

in the process. Sometimes we tied a string to a coconut and swung it in a circle above our heads while she jumped high up after it as it flew past. She soon discovered that digging in the sand was a most rewarding game, since the deeper the hole the wetter and cooler it became and therefore the nicer to roll in. Often she dragged long strands of seaweed along, entangling herself in it till she looked like some odd sea monster. But crabs provided her with the best fun of all. Towards sunset the beach became alive with these little

pink creatures shuffling sideways in order to get from their holes to the water, only to be washed ashore again a moment later. Persistently they shuffled, only to be thrown back again, until finally their patience was rewarded and they grabbed some piece of delicious seaweed and pulled it into their hole before the next wave was able to carry it off. Elsa did not make things easier for the busy creatures; she would rush from one to the other, invariably getting nipped in the nose, but undeterred she pounced again, only to be nipped once more. To the crabs' credit be it recorded that of all Elsa's opponents they were the only ones, not excluding elephants, buffaloes and rhinos, which stood their ground. Sideways-on they waited in front of their holes, one pink claw erect, and however cunningly Elsa tried to outwit them, they were always quicker than she was and her soft nose got punctured again.

Like all holidays, ours had passed much too quickly, but by the time we went home we had acquired a deep tan and Elsa, owing to her sea bathing, had developed a beautiful silky coat.

CHUT, THE KANGAROO

From the book "Wilderness Orphan"

By DOROTHY COTTRELL

> The setting of this gentle – and fierce! – story is, of course, Australia.
> When the three men had finished skinning their game – two kangaroos –
> they took a last look around. Suddenly one of them saw the infant "joey"
> whose mother had been killed the night before.

"Jove!" said the man. "There's a little fellow!"

He pounced upon Chut, who simply shrank into himself and waited for the last spasm of the terror which was death.

"He's a little beauty," said the man. "I'm going to take him home to my wife." He held Chut up ridiculously by the scruff of the neck and poked him with his finger. Then the man looked puzzled. "He's all scratched and he's been cut across the back – looks like an eagle's had him . . . Say, I guess he must have belonged to the doe that got away last night! Poor little nipper!"

"Let's take him and give him a drink!" the other men suggested. Gathering up the skins, they moved off round the head of the dam, Chut hanging limp and hopeless under the big man's arm.

At the camp, back over the ridge, there was discussion as to how the baby should be fed and some facetious suggestions of sending for Dr. Holt's Book on Infant Feeding. Then the first man said: "He won't drink unless he's upside down . . ." So they got an old pair of trousers and tied a knot in one leg at the knee, and hung the trousers to a tree limb by the back strap. Then they held Chut up before it. He looked at it in confusion.

"Better let him get in himself," said the big man. He gave Chut a friendly pinch. It worked. Instinctively Chut grasped the edge of the trousers, lowered his head, and bracing his hoppers against the big man's stomach, turned his dexterous somersault into the warm depths of the leg! Once again he was swinging as a kangaroo should swing. He was enclosed; safe. He gave a feeble, twittering chitter.

One of the other men stepped forward and presented him with the end of a bit of insulating rubber, from which the wire had been withdrawn, and whose other end was in a tin of milk.

Chut sucked, sucked again. Milk was in his mouth. He gave little ticking sounds of bliss, and, still drinking, he fell asleep in the maternal embrace of the trouser leg.

Chut's wound healed. The men were good to him. He learned the new smells of fire-smoke, and potatoes roasting in ashes; the mellow smell of coffee and the sharp tang of tea, the odors of frizzling bacon and grilling chops; of tobacco smoke by a camp fire under stars; and the sneeziness of raw flour, and the smell of men. He learned that fire was hot and kerosene nasty. His ears attuned themselves to new sounds, for the men were as noisy as the wilderness was silent. Clatter of plates, loud jests and louder laughter, galloping of horses and clanging music of horse-bells, ceased to appall him.

When, after a month's work on the lower run, the big man returned home, Chut went with him, swinging securely in one leg of a pair of old trousers attached to the man's saddle. Arrived at the small, tree-set homestead, the man was met by his young wife; and Chut observing the meeting through a cigarette hole in the trouser leg, sensed that it was affectionate.

"I've brought you home a baby!" the big man said untying the old trousers from the pommel of the saddle, and handing them to her – one of the legs showing plumply bulged. She took the garment hesitatingly, peering into the top, perceived Chut where he waited in bright-eyed, velvet-furred minuteness, and exclaimed: "Oh, the darling, sweet, tiny thing!"

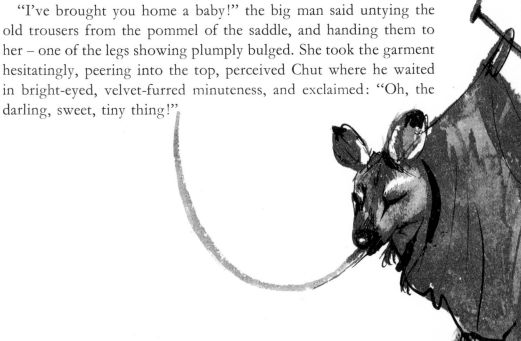

The man dismounted, and stepped up to her.

"He is so little!" she said.

"And so soft and fat."

At that the man took her in his arms.

"What," she said, "will we call him?"

But, squeezed between the big man and his wife, Chut was very uncomfortable. He gave a surprisingly loud and indignant cry of protest. "Chut! Chut! Chut-ch-ch-ch-ch!"

So he was called "Chut", which prior to this time had simply been his staple of conversation and announcement of his presence.

During the day he followed the girl about like a little dog. At night he slept in the trousers which swung by the big outside fire-place – these habiliments coming to be known as "Chut's pants".

He would come when the woman called him, and somersault neatly into her lap as she sat on the steps. There, lying on his back, he took his supper to the accompaniment of small kicks of pleasure.

He was also promoted to all the dignity of a real baby's bottle instead of the bit of insulating tube fastened to a condensed milk tin with which the men had nourished him in camp. The dogs were introduced to him one by one, it being forcefully explained to them that he was taboo.

There was soft green grass in which he might roll, and many trailing pepper trees beneath which to play small solitary games. In short, his world was eminently satisfactory – save for one thing.

There was at the homestead a ridiculously fat, excessively bumptious lamb, by name William Mutton. To William had belonged the baby's bottle before Chut took it over, and William harbored a dark and bitter resentment at the loss of his bottle. He was an incredibly greedy lamb. And, although fed to repletion, he was forever sucking at the woman's fingers, at her apron strings, at the tassels of blinds – anything. A moment after having eaten until he could eat no more, he called pitifully of his semi-starvation. To see anyone else eat appeared to cause him pain.

"That lamb," said the big man, "is not, I fear, of a generous turn of mind. He might even be described as a little grasping."

At least, to see Chut being nourished appeared to sear the very soul of William Mutton. Chut had been eager to be friendly. Upon one of the first occasions when he had ventured on a little walk by himself, he had come upon the lamb around a trailing pepper branch. The baleful gleam in William Mutton's eye meant nothing to him. All he saw was a creature of approximately his own size who might possibly want to sport a little.

Chut drew himself up to his now twenty-five-inch height, and standing poised upon the arch of his lower tail and the tips of his toes he gave a few stiff, bouncing little sidehops – the kangaroo's invitation to play.

"Chut!" he remarked affably. "Chut! Ch-ch!"

William's head dropped lower. He focused evilly upon the cream-velvet rotundity of Chut's stomach. Then, with a malevolent "Baa", he charged upon the little kangaroo.

His round woolly head met Chut's silk-furred stomach with a resonant plop. Chut grunted and fell, kicking, while William strolled triumphantly about his business without even deigning to look back.

After that he took especial pains to make the little kangaroo's life wretched. He specialized in knocking Chut down from different directions and in varying localities. He learned his victim's weaknesses and played upon them . . .

Persistent persecution will, of course, develop wariness in the most confiding creature, and as Chut grew older he became harder to catch. On the other hand, if William's butts became less frequent, they became harder: for William was a particularly hefty young sheep and in addition he was growing horns – only nubby buds as yet, but distinctly uncomfortable when applied to Chut's person.

Then, about the time that, greatly to his own surprise, Chut outgrew his trouser leg, the big man, whose name Chut now knew was Tom Henton, brought in two little does who were just a shade smaller than Chut had been at the time of his capture.

And the woman whom everyone but Tom Henton called Mrs. Henton christened them Zodie and Blue Baby, and Chut promptly adopted them both. He would sit for twenty minutes at a time chitting and whispering into the mouths of their sleeping bags. He nosed them, and pulled in a manly, masterful way at their ears.

When they were old enough to come out to play, he romped with them, and at times put his little arms round both their necks so that the three small heads were drawn close together. Then he led them upon little gallops beneath the trees.

Of the two little does, Blue Baby was his darling. For as gentleman allegedly prefer blondes, so male kangaroos seem melted by a blue tone in a lady's fur: experienced old kangaroo hunters having often noticed that amongst all the mouse-hued harem an "old man" will make a pet of a blue doe.

And Blue Baby was furred in an exquisite shade of smoke blue, brighter than the bluest of squirrel fur, and her stomach and chest were clear, cream-velvet. Her slender little tail, hoppers and hands, were dark, her eyes dark and dewy-soft. But for some reason she was slightly lame.

She could travel all right on her hoppers and hands, but when she attempted to hop in an upright position she stumbled and fell. Hence she was always left behind in the races. And Chut would always circle back for her, and pass and repass her – as though he did not want her to be left out.

When she too outgrew the trousers, he slept with one little arm about her neck, their attitudes touchingly like those of sleeping children.

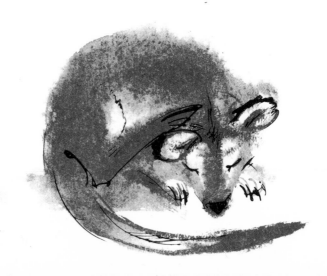

As an evil shadow on the sunshine of young romance hovered the malevolent-eyed Mutton, always ready to charge upon the unguarded Chut and knock the wind out of him.

But Chut was growing miraculously fast now. His chubbiness had gone from him, likewise the legginess of youth that followed it. He was nowhere near his full growth – would not reach it for a long time yet – but he was strong-boned, erect, with the muscles swelling deeply beneath the skin of his forearms and back. When he drew himself up, he was almost as tall as Mrs. Henton. But at her call his great body still somersaulted innocently into her lap, and, when he could inveigle her into giving it to him, he still adored his bottle. He still lay on his back in the sun and played with his toes, and he still had an infantile attachment for the pair of trousers which had been his foster-mother.

After the manner of kangaroos he was consumingly curious. He wanted to see everything. He tasted everything, and loved bread and sugar.

Gentle and awkward on the slippery oilcloth, the three kangaroos would come begging about the dinner table for pieces of sugared bread, which they had been taught to carry outside before eating – although they often fell to temptation and snatched little bites as they went.

One day they had just got their precious sweetened bread, and carried it out beneath the big pepper tree, when the marauding Mutton bore down upon them.

Chut and Zodie hopped out of the way, still holding their crusts, but Blue Baby was clumsy and in her agitation she dropped her bread.

Had William Mutton contented himself with merely taking the bread, it is doubtful if Chut would have noticed, but William, who in the past had always confined his attacks to Chut, suddenly decided that Blue Baby would do as well. And, with an evil "Baa", he charged her – sending her sprawling to the grass, chittering little exclamations of fright!

Chut looked up. Blue Baby chittered more alarmedly.

Chut dropped his bread and drew himself up onto toes and lower tail-arch, and made a few little bouncing dancing steps: a kangaroo's invitation to play or fight.

William Mutton had seized Blue Baby's bit of bread. Blue Baby still lay on her back in the grass too astonished and frightened to rise.

Chut danced up to the sheep, his arms hanging out from his sides like a belligerent man's, his ribs expanded.

"Chut!" he cried harshly. "Chut! Chut! Chut!"

"Baa!" said William Mutton, contemptuously masticating. Next moment he was grabbed by the backwool, and one of Chut's long hind toes kicked him dexterously in the side, tearing out a hunk of wool as it ripped downward.

Like most bullies, William was an arrant coward. He bleated and leapt for safety. Chut clawed for his fat rump as he went, and pulled out more wool. William gathered pulsing momentum of baa-punctuated bounds. And Chut followed him, trying vainly for another kick – for anything as low as a sheep is a most awkward thing for a kangaroo to fight.

William fled wildly, crying for undeserved help. The swimming pool lay before them. At its edge William, who dreaded water, tried to wheel, and at the same moment gave a foolish, prancing rear-up!

This was fatal. A kangaroo cannot kick well unless it can embrace the thing it is kicking. William's semi-leap brought him to the perfect height for Chut's best attentions. Chut's hands clutched the miserable sheep's neck, his strong-muscled arms tightened like virgin rubber as he clasped the writhing form of Mutton to his chest. With "chuts" and nickers of rage he delivered a whirlwind of kicks to his victim's stomach.

They were his first fighting kicks, and poorly directed – which was as well for William – but they drew bleats and wool at each application.

Then Chut lost his balance, released his hold for a moment, and William Mutton made a frantic leap for safety – into the pool!

Tom Henton, who had been an amused and astonished spectator of the fight, fished him out again. He emerged a sadder and wiser sheep, to whom a kangaroo's stomach was forever after invisible.

But Chut had tasted the hot wine of his own strength. He wanted someone to wrestle with! During the next days he hopped pompously about the garden enclosure, with his arms swinging a little out from his sides, his chest expanded and his spine curving backward with his erectness. He stood in front of Tom Henton as he came in of an evening, and made little sparring, sideward hops on the extreme tips of his toes and ridged arch of his lower-tail.

One night the man laughed, saying: "All right then!" and put on boxing gloves to spar with the great young kangaroo. Mrs. Henton had viewed the proceeding with alarm, for a kangaroo can disembowel a man or dog with a single scythe-rip of his hooked foot. But it was soon obvious that Chut fully understood the playful nature of the battle. He would no more have thought of letting his strength go than the man would have dreamed of putting his full weight behind a blow to Chut's jaw.

They clinched and swayed, they sparred and side-stepped, until

Tom leapt back to wipe the sweat from his streaming face, and Chut panted, and cooled his arms by licking them to the semblance of dark rubber.

After this they wrestled almost every evening, and so "boxing" was added to Chut's tricks. At the end of a match, if he had "played" well, he got his little bit of bread and sugar – which he held in both hands and smeared disgustingly about his face.

It happened that the summer had been a very busy one for Tom Henton, and so he had engaged a "yard-man" to look after the cows, and the wood-chopping, and the home vegetable garden. The youth who performed these duties was not prepossessing, his manner alternating between over-familiarity and sullenness, while his progress was exasperatingly deliberate. A seemingly permanent cigarette drooped from his lower lip, and he did not remove it as he spoke.

Still, labor was hard to get, and Tom Henton decided to keep the man until after the shearing.

William Mutton, who had no decent pride, would follow the yard-man about in the hope of sneaking something from the fowls' bucket, but Chut ignored the youth's existence.

At least he ignored it until the shearing-time came.

The shearing shed and the sheep yards were some half-mile from the house, but dust clouds stirred up from the drafting pens had come to Chut's nostrils with exciting scents of heat and sheep trailing from them. He caught far, murmurous bleatings, stockwhip cracks, distant shoutings...

And Chut wanted to go and see the shearing! He plainly indicated as much as Tom Henton was riding out of a morning: placing one horny, confiding hand upon the man's stirrup in hint that he was coming too. When, in spite of this, he was left behind, he hopped up and down inside the enclosure fence, thumping his twenty-pound tail deliberately and loudly upon the ground as an intimation of his extreme displeasure and agitation.

Tom Henton had given very definite instructions that the big kangaroo was not to be let out during shearing. He didn't want any tricks played upon Chut, and shearer-men have an odd sense of humor. Also there was always the chance of a sudden fright temporarily stampeding the kangaroo into the bush, and there he might be shot in mistake for a wild 'roo.

"Keep the gates shut," said Tom to the yardman. "And be dead sure they're fastened!" The youth spat and said "O. K.," but he had already resolved to take Chut down to the shed and stage a demonstration fight for a shilling-a-man admission.

To do this he waited until a Sunday afternoon, when Tom Henton was away bringing in sheep for Monday's "run", and Mrs. Henton was lying down asleep.

Chut was also dozing under a pepper tree, with his legs sticking absurdly skyward, when the yardman whispered his name and enticed him with bread. But he took no notice until he saw the man open the gate. Then he followed, and continued following all the

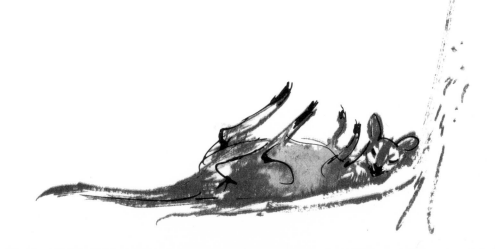

way to the shed: hopping behind the yardman's pony. At the shed he was embarassed by the numbers of people and by the great wool-smelling iron rooms.

And because the yardman was at least familiar, Chut followed him more closely still.

The yardman collected his shillings, and then led the big, puzzled kangaroo into the wool room, while the audience seated itself upon the stacked bales of wool.

The yardman fastened on Chut's gloves and put on gloves himself: then he stepped out in a fighting attitude, saying: "Come on, Boy!"

Chut didn't want to come on, however. He was rather frightened by the laughter, the voices, and the smoke haze. Also he was particular about the people with whom he fought. His boxing was a love-game he played with Tom Henton.

"Put 'em up!" said the yardman, tapping Chut lightly upon the cheek. Chut sat far back on his haunches and chutted offendedly: a small sound in appealing contrast to his size. The man danced up and down before him and poked him in the ribs. Chut protested with dignity, but made no attempt to fight.

Grumbling began amongst the members of the audience.

"Hey, where's my shilling?" "Aw, I'm going home." "This is a dead show!" "*That* the best he can do?"

The yardman began to lose his temper. The fool beast fought quick enough when he wanted to! He was going to fight now! He hit ·Chut rather ungently in the lower ribs. Chut grunted and looked about with great soft eyes – appealing for fair play! He was not hurting this man, and the man was getting rough with him!

Still he obviously had no intention of sparring. He was a picture of gentle, slightly pompous, and much-offended courtesy. He looked about for Tom or Mrs. Henton...

"Garn! He's no fighter!" yelled the men. "Where's them shillin's?"

The yardman was hot, nervous and exasperated. His audience was threatening to walk out on him. Unnoticed by any of the spec-

76

tators, he snatched the live cigarette from his lips, and holding it hidden in his glove he pressed the glowing tip upon Chut's sensitive nose. Pressed it hard, twisted it.

The sequel happened so quickly that no one was sure of just how Chut got the silly gloves off. But next second he was holding the screaming yardman in his powerful hug, and, having torn the youth's trousers off, was operating on his shirt-tail to the accompaniment of a ripping, rag-bag sort of sound!

As the shirt vanished, Chut's great-toe plied artistically for a hold upon the yardman's abdomen. With his forehand he clawed the yardman's hair. His eyes had a new, murderous light. He shook and bent the man in his embrace!...

Then half the men in the shed were on him. Beating at him with rails, prodding him with wool hooks.

He dropped the frantic and badly clawed yardman, and wheeled – to receive a bewildering rain of blows!

His swift anger was already over. All he wanted was to go home. He burst through the threatening circle and hopped majestically out of the wool room door, gathering momentum as he went, and moving homeward, not with the frantic thirty-feet-at-a-bound of a frightened doe, but rhythmically covering a steady fifteen feet at a hop. One man fired after him, but the shots went wide.

It was at this stage that Tom Henton rode up to the shed, to be horrified at the tale of Chut's ferocity and the spectacle of the bleeding man. With relief he found that no vital injury had been done, but it was with a heavy heart that he at last rode home. The shearers, none of whom had observed the cigarette outrage, had assured him that the yardman had simply been inviting Chut to a friendly sparring bout!

If Chut was going to make unprovoked attacks like that, he was not safe . . .

Mrs. Henton was likewise shocked at the account of the yardman's injuries. But she refused to believe that Chut's anger had been unprovoked.

"We simply couldn't shoot him!" she cried. "Why, if he could tell us what happened, he could very likely explain everything! Oh Tom, he is so dear and funny!"

"We can't get his side of it," said the man. "And the fact remains that if he hadn't been beaten off he might have killed someone."

"You *can't* shoot him!"

"I can't see how we can keep him. I'd be afraid for you, honey. Afraid to have him loose around – and I'd sooner shoot him than cage him."

"I know he wouldn't hurt anyone unless they hurt him!" she cried. But Tom looked away with troubled face.

"You know how we would feel if there was an accident," he said.

"Well, don't do it yet – after dinner – not yet."

The evening meal passed in heavy silence. They were both thinking about what would have to be done. As they rose from the table the woman began to cry. She said: "Oh Tom, you can't!"

"I'll have to," said the man, still looking away from her. Suddenly she took his arm.

"Come and see him, before we make up our minds!"

They passed along the veranda to the old outside fireplace. Chut was lying on his back beside the faded and shredded remains of the

81

trousers that had mothered him. His eyes were soft and sad with dreams.

As the man and woman looked down at him, he reached up great arms to catch his great toe.

With tears and laughter mingling in her voice, the woman said: "Oh Tom, he can't be dangerous! Look at him!"

"He doesn't look it," said the man, tears gleaming in his eyes.

Just then the girl fell swiftly to her knees, her fingers searching the velvet fur just above the kangaroo's quivering nose. "Look!" she cried. "Look!"

The man held the lamp down. On Chut's nose there was a small, deep, raw pit, eaten into the flesh. About the edges of the rawness the hair was singed and burnt.

"Couldn't that have been done by a cigarette?" she questioned.

"You bet it was!" he replied.

"Well," she said, "that's *his* side of the story for you, Tom!" Then she reached down and clasped her arms about Chut's neck. "Oh, I am so glad! So glad!"

They stood up.

"I," said the man, "am sorry . . ."

"What do you *mean?*" questioned the girl.

"I'm sorry Chut's done such a good job with the yardman that he hasn't left me a chance!" said Tom Henton, his fingers lingering about the swell of his bicep.

Later the girl slipped back and gave Chut a whole half-loaf of bread with melted sugar. He ate it placidly and blissfully, with small tickings of pleasure. Sugar ran down his chin and got into his fur. He was soon perfectly horrible with sugar and covered with crumbs. Nevertheless, his mistress stooped and kissed him.

MR. CAT DISAPPEARS

From the book "Mr. Cat"

By GEORGE FREEDLEY

For some sixteen years, Mr. Cat, a sociable Persian, lived with the Curator of the New York Public Library's Theatre Collection, in Manhattan's East Fifties. He was known to a wide circle of stage personalities, and to shopkeepers, doormen and friends whose provinces he had explored on his own. In a book about him, *Mr. Cat*, George Freedley tells of his remarkable cat's almost final adventure.

At this moment it seems forever ago that Mr. Cat disappeared for a second time. It was on a June morning that I awoke early and there were no signs of him beside my bed. I was more annoyed than apprehensive, however, as I dressed and left for the day.

"He's probably fallen asleep on the roof," I grumbled. "Or else he's gone and gotten himself trapped in somebody's apartment again." He *had* done that once and had to wait two days until they returned from their week-end.

For the past few nights he had been in and out of the apartment so often via the fire escape, that I felt sure I would hear his trumpeting call even before I left the building. And of course, he now wore a harness with his identification so he couldn't get lost.

At lunchtime, I telephoned the superintendent. He looked into the apartment and reported it empty. At dinner time when he had not returned and his food was still untouched, my alarm grew, but I realized that there was little to do but sit and hope. I went to bed shortly after dinner, but every sound in the old house awakened me with the vain hope that The Prodigal had returned.

83

At last, I had to face the inevitable and telephoned the ASPCA and once again placed advertisements in the newspapers. No Persian had been turned in, and no reply came from the advertisements except from friends and neighbors who called to inquire.

One lady telephoned and said she was positive that she had seen a Persian hiding under an automobile in Beekman Place nearly a mile from his home. She had tried to coax him out, recognizing that he was "somebody's" but he had gotten away. I thanked her though I doubted that it was Mr. Cat.

With the help of a friend, I placed a mimeographed description of the lost one, complete with departure time and date, telephone number and my home and office telephone numbers. We left them in all the mailboxes of the neighborhood, and the Beekman Place area as well. We even left them in Fifth Avenue and Madison Avenue shops and office buildings, remembering Mr. Cat's last experience.

The local police were alerted until they must have been sick of my voice. Our building superintendent spread the word to all his confreres at their local "club", a bar on Lexington Avenue. (Unfortunately, as it turned out, *one* superintendent did not belong to their club.) They neglected no rumor, whether it was of Persian or Maltese, gray, white or what have you.

And now days grew into weeks until it got to the point that a kindly inquiry became a source of pain. When I answered the telephone now, it was sure to be some friend asking if there were any news. My replies got less and less polite, though perhaps more resigned. Where was Mr. Cat?

When it came to the fifth week, I could no longer believe that I would ever see himself again. I could not believe that he would ever consent to accept a new home, no matter what inducements were offered. The best I could hope was that he had been kidnapped again, and some day would get free and find his way back to me.

As the fifth week drew to a close, the telephone rang at lunch time. A strange voice asked, "Are you Mr. Freedley? Have you lost a cat?"

84

My voice shook as I answered that I was, and I had. "Have – have you found him?"

"I found his collar," the voice replied, "with his name, and yours, so I called you up. I'm the superintendent over at 16 East 56th, the Fiberglass place. We're putting in airconditioning and the hole in the floor in the secretary's room was covered with a board. We are re-flooring tomorrow, so I lifted up the board and looked down the hole and found this harness."

"Do you think . . ." I ventured.

"Don't get your hopes up," said the superintendent. "I called through the hole and there was no answer. You say it was almost six weeks ago, and it's been hot as blazes. Maybe he *was* there and got away. Maybe he *is* there, but . . ."

I could not understand why he had not gotten the mimeographed paper we had left at every building including his, but there was no time for that now. The office closed at five, and I was to come over then.

It was the longest afternoon I ever spent. I tried to be rational. Six weeks! And the hottest July we had had for years. It was only common sense that Mr. Cat couldn't be alive after being shut up there for six weeks without food or water. If he were there, would his inquiring eyes still be bright and ready to greet me?

I dressed in my oldest clothes in anticipation of climbing between floors, and I hauled out his old carrier as well as some of his dangle toys. The sight of them made my eyes grow wet. Cold reason made me bring along an old silence cloth as well. Cats had been known to go mad . . .

A lone secretary was at the desk when I arrived at the Fiberglass Building with the superintendent. First, we called up the ASPCA: "Is it true," I asked, "that you rescue cats from between buildings or from under floors?"

They assured me that they would come and tear up the whole floor if there were the slightest hope.

I lifted up the board and called his name.

"Mr. Cat," I called. "Mr. Cat."

There was silence. Then from afar, a faint mew answered me! Six weeks!

I was shaking with excitement as I continued to call down into the hole and spoke to him. The face of the superintendent was a study as he lent me his flashlight. The secretary's jaw dropped open.

I knelt down and put my hand into the hole. A small paw patted my hand.

I was afraid to do more lest in his fear Mr. Cat would withdraw altogether. I dangled his favorite cellophane ball and I saw him slowly appear. Slowly, I drew the ball towards me, and slowly he followed it. What were the memories that went through his mind as he saw and heard that homely wad of cellophane which had once been such a source of innocent pleasure to a lovely kitten? He trembled and the whole of his body came into view. I dropped the cord and gently but firmly grabbed at him and pulled him up.

Then, in my amazement, I almost dropped him! He had weighed almost fifteen pounds when I lost him; he had wasted away until he was little more than one pound. His long fur had concealed his emaciation until I held him in my arms. Only his eyes seemed larger and brighter, but that of course was in comparison with the rest of his frame.

Then he talked to me quite plainly: "Well, it's time you got here," he seemed to say. "Where on earth have you been?"

"Six weeks," marveled the superintendent.

We called the ASPCA and cancelled our request for help but the wagon was already on the way, so a friend of mine was asked to come by and inform them what had happened. I gently laid Mr. Cat into the carrier, using the silence cloth as a cushion. Thank heavens, I had not needed it!

What passers-by on Madison Avenue in that early August dusk

thought when they saw a man hurry by with an animal carrier, a handful of toys, and tears streaming down his face, I shall never know. Nor shall I care. Mr. Cat was safe.

When I got him home, I lifted him out of the carrier and set him on his feet. He tried to follow me into the kitchen but he sagged over from weakness. I held him in my arms as I warmed a little milk and put him down besides the saucer. He smelled it, but made no effort to touch it. He had forgotten how to eat.

Finally, I dipped my finger in the milk and held it to his lips. He licked it like a newly weaned kitten. I repeated this until he gradually got accustomed to lap the milk himself. In this way, I fed him every ten minutes for two hours until we both dropped off to sleep.

The friend who had waited for the ASPCA wagon came by the next morning. He told me that the attendant had listened with impassive face to the piteous tale and had jotted down on his report sheet the laconic notation:

"Got cat out himself."

WOL HELPS OUT

From the book "Owls in the Family"

By FARLEY MOWAT

When the Canadian writer, Farley Mowat, was growing up in Saskatchewan, Canada, he and his schoolmate, Bruce, were encouraged by their natural-science teacher to hunt for the nest of great horned owls. Out of this searching, Farley gained a pet owlet that became the enormous and intrepid Wol (the name of the owl in A. A. Milne's Pooh stories) and a timid owl whom he called Weeps. Mr. Mowat has written of these companions of his boyhood in *The Dog Who Wouldn't Be* and *Owls in the Family*. Mutt was his black-and-white almost-setter.

The banks of the Saskatchewan River were very steep where the river ran through the prairie to the south of Saskatoon; and about two miles downstream from the city was a perfect place for digging caves. Bruce and Murray and I had our summer headquarters down there, in an old cave some hobos had dug a long time ago. They had fixed it up with logs and pieces of wood so it wouldn't collapse. You have to be careful of caves, because if they don't have good strong logs to hold up the roof, the whole thing can fall down and kill you. This was a good cave we had, though; my Dad had even come there and looked it over to make sure it was safe for us.

It had a door made of a piece of tin-roofing, and there was a smoke-stack going up through the ceiling. Inside was a sort of bench where you could lie down, and we had two old butter-tubs for chairs. We put dry hay down on the floor for a carpet, and under the hay was a secret hole where we could hide anything that was specially valuable.

The river ran only a hop-skip-and-a-jump from the door of the cave. There was a big sand bar close by which made a backwater where the current was slow enough for swimming. Standing right beside the swimming hole was the biggest cottonwood tree in the whole of Saskatchewan. One of its branches stuck straight out over the water, and there were old marks on it where a rope had cut into

89

the bark. An Indian who was being chased by the Mounties, a long, long time ago, was supposed to have hanged himself on that branch so the Mounties wouldn't catch him alive.

We used to go to our cave a couple of times a week during the summer holidays, and usually we took the owls along. Wol had learned how to ride on the handle bars of my bicycle; but Weeps couldn't keep his balance there, so we built a kind of box for him and tied it to the carrier behind the seat. Mutt and Rex used to come, too, chasing cows whenever they got a chance, or racing away across the prairie after jack rabbits.

We would bike out to the end of Third Avenue and then along an old Indian trail which ran along the top of the riverbank. When we got close to the cave we would hide our bikes in the willows and then climb down the bank and follow a secret path. There were some pretty tough kids in Saskatoon, and we didn't want them to find our cave if we could help it.

Wol loved those trips. All the way out he would bounce up and down on the handle bars, hooting to himself with excitement, or hooting out insults at any passing dog. When we came to the place

where we hid the bikes, he would fly up into the poplars and follow us through the tops of the trees. He usually stayed pretty close, though; because, if he didn't, some crows would be sure to spot him and then they would call up all the other crows for miles around and try to mob him. When that happened, he would come zooming down to the cave and bang on the door with his beak until we let him in.

He wasn't afraid of the crows; it was just that **he couldn't fight** back when they tormented him. As for Weeps, he **usually stayed** right in the cave, where he felt safe.

One summer afternoon, when we were at the cave, we decided to go for a swim. The three of us shucked off our clothes and raced for the sand bar, hollering at each other: "Last one in's a Dutchman!"

In half a minute we were in the water, splashing around and rolling in the slippery black mud along the edge of the sand bar. It was great stuff to fight with. Nice and soft and slithery, it packed into mushy mud-balls that made a wonderful splash when they hit something.

Whenever we went swimming, Wol would come along and find a perch in the Hanging Tree where he could watch the fun. He would get out on the big limb that hung over the water, and the more fuss and noise we made, the more excited he became. He would walk back and forth along the limb, *hoo-hooing* and ruffling his feathers, and you could tell he felt he was missing out on the fun.

This particular day he couldn't stand it any longer, so he came down out of the tree and waddled right to the river's edge.

We were skylarking on the sand bar when I saw him, so I gave out a yell: "Hey, Wol! C'mon there, Wol, old owl! C'mon out here!"

Of course I thought he would fly across the strip of open water and light on the dry sand where we were playing. But I forgot Wol had never had any experience with water before, except in his drinking bowl at home.

He got his experience in a hurry. Instead of spreading his wings, he lifted up one foot very deliberately and started to walk across the water toward us.

It didn't take him long to find out he couldn't do it. There was an almighty splash, and spray flew every which way. By the time we raced across and fished him out, he was half-drowned and about the sickest bird you ever saw. His feathers were plastered down until he looked as skinny as a plucked chicken. The slimy black mud hadn't improved his looks much, either.

I carried him ashore, but he didn't thank me for it. His feelings were hurt worse than he was, and after he had shaken most of the water out of his feathers, he went gallumphing off through the woods toward home, on foot (he was too wet to fly), without a backward glance.

Toward the middle of July, Bruce and I got permission from our parents to spend a night in the cave. Murray couldn't come because his mother wouldn't let him. We took Wol and Weeps with us, and of course we had both dogs.

In the afternoon we went for a hike over the prairie, looking for birds. Mutt, who was running ahead of us, flushed a prairie chicken off her nest. There were ten eggs in the nest, and they were just hatching out.

We sat down beside the nest and watched. In an hour's time, seven of the little chickens had hatched before our eyes. It was pretty exciting to see, and Wol seemed just as curious about it as we were. Then all of a sudden three of the newly hatched little birds slipped out of the nest and scuttled straight for Wol. Before he could move they were underneath him, crowding against his big feet, and *peep-peeping* happily. I guess they thought he was their mother, because they hadn't seen their real mother yet.

Wol was so surprised he didn't know what to do. He kept lifting up one foot and then the other to shake off the little ones. When the other four babies joined the first three, Wol began to get nervous. But finally he seemed to resign himself to being a mother, and he fluffed his feathers out and lowered himself very gently to the ground.

Bruce and I nearly died laughing. The sight of the baby prairie chickens popping their heads out through Wol's feathers, and that great big beak of his snapping anxiously in the air right over their heads, was the silliest thing I've ever seen. I guess Wol knew it was silly, too, but he couldn't figure how to get out of the mess he was

in. He kept looking at me as if he were saying: "For Heaven's sake, DO something!"

I don't know how long he would have stayed there, but we began to worry that the real mother might not find her chicks, so I finally lifted him up and put him on my shoulder, and we went back to the cave for supper.

We'd had a good laugh at Wol, but he had the laugh on us before the day was done.

After we had eaten, we decided to go down to the riverbank and wait for the sun to set. A pair of coyotes lived on the opposite bank of the river, and every evening just at sunset one of them would climb a little hill and sit there howling. It was a scary sound, but we liked it because it made us feel that this was the olden times, and the prairie belonged to us, to the buffaloes and the Indians, and to the prairie wolves.

Wol was sitting in the Hanging Tree, and Rex and Mutt had gone off somewhere on a hunting trip of their own. It was growing dusk when we heard a lot of crashing in the trees behind us. We turned around just as two big kids came into sight. They were two of the toughest kids in Saskatoon. If they hadn't come on us so suddenly, we would have been running before they ever saw us. But now it was too late to run – they would have caught us before we could go ten feet. The only thing we could do was sit where we were and hope they would leave us alone.

What a hope *that* was! They came right over and one of them reached down and grabbed Bruce and started to twist his arm behind his back.

"Listen, you little rats," he said, "we heard you got a cave some-place down here. You're too young to own a cave, so we're taking over. Show us where it is, or I'll twist your arm right off!"

The other big kid made a grab for me, but I slipped past him and was just starting to run when he stuck his foot out and tripped me. Then he sat on me.

"Say, Joe," he said to his pal, "I got an idea. Either these kids

95

tell us where the cave is, or we tie 'em to the Hanging Tree and leave 'em there all night with the Injun's ghost.''

Just then the coyote across the river gave a howl. All four of us jumped a little, what with the talk of ghosts – but Joe said: ''That ain't nothing. Just a coyote howling. You going to tell us, kid? Or do we tie you to the tree?''

Bruce and I knew they were only trying to scare us, but we were scared all right. I was just opening my mouth to tell them where the cave was when Wol took a hand in things.

He had been sitting on the big limb of the Hanging Tree and, since it was almost dark by then, he looked like a big white blob up there. I don't think he'd been paying much attention to what was happening on the ground below him, but when that coyote howled, he must have thought it was some kind of challenge. He opened his beak and gave the Owl Hunting Scream.

Did you ever hear a horned owl scream? Usually they do it at night to scare any mice or rabbits that happen to be hiding near into jumping or running. Then the owl swoops down and grabs them. If you've ever heard an owl scream, you'll know it's just about the most scary sound in all the world.

When Wol cut loose, it made even my skin creep – and I knew what it was; but the two big kids didn't know.

Their heads jerked up, and they saw the ghostly white shape that was Wol up there in the Hanging Tree. And then they were off and running. They went right through the poplar woods like a couple of charging buffaloes, and we could still hear them breaking brush when they were half a mile away. My guess is that they ran all the way to Saskatoon.

When they were out of hearing, Bruce stood up and began rubbing his arm. Then he looked at Wol.

''Boy!'' he said. ''You sure scared those two roughnecks silly! But did you have to scare *me* right out of my skin, too?''

''Hoo-HOO-hoo-hoo-hoo-HOO!'' Wol chuckled as he floated down out of the tree and lit upon my shoulder.

THE EASTER LAMB

From the book "Steffos and his Easter Lamb"

By AN RUTGERS VAN DER LOEFF

The Greek shepherd boy, Steffos, suddenly finds he cannot bear to part
with the family's Easter lamb, due to be slaughtered the next evening.
Meanwhile an archaeological expedition has come in a bus to his village
and a reward is being offered for any information about an ancient palace
thought to be buried there. Steffos remembers a strange stone his brother,
Dilemachos, once showed him and guides the party to it hoping, for his
reward, to be allowed to escape with his lamb on the archaeologists' bus.
But first he discovers his special feeling about the tiny lamb.

A thousand and one thoughts flitted through his mind as his bare
feet pattered through the soft dust.

Maybe I can run away with the lamb in the bus... I can ask
whether they need a boy for odd jobs... I can say that I'll polish
their shoes every day. People like that are sure to wear shoes...

I can say that the lamb has to go to my uncle in Athens... I can say that a butcher in Athens has bought the lamb and that we have to...

That is how Steffos's thoughts ran on.

The little grey-haired professor came and sat down beside him. "Tell me," she said quietly, "why do you want to go away with that lamb? Isn't it your family's Easter lamb?"

Steffos did not answer.

"Or has your mother told you to take it to the city to sell it?"

Before he knew what he was doing, Steffos had nodded his head.

"How much can you get for a lamb like that in the city?" the professor went on.

Steffos bit his lip. He did not have the foggiest idea. But he blurted out the very first amount that came into his head. It was the price that neighbour Andronicus had received for three piglets he had sold recently.

The learned lady looked at him inquiringly. Steffos was mighty pleased that she was not wearing glasses. But maybe she saw more than he thought.

She looked again at the Easter lamb which had dropped off to sleep at Steffos's feet. Then she stood up. A few minutes later Steffos saw her talking seriously to the other professor, who was a man twice her height. Others gathered round them and they all put their learned heads together. But when the Greek driver was finally consulted, he began to wave his arms violently. He rolled his head from side to side so that the wreath nearly toppled down on to his red face. "It is strictly forbidden to transport animals in my bus!" he shouted so loudly that the sound echoed between the hills.

Then the little professor came back to Steffos. "No," she said, "No, it can't be done. But you'll receive the reward, you know. You've a right to that. And it is twice as much as you would get for the lamb in the city. What do you say to that?"

If she had expected Steffos to be pleased, she was wrong. He

101

tried to pretend he was, but his heart was not in it. A lump rose in his throat. What good was money to him? What good was a king's castle, if he could not save his lamb?

"I'll shine your shoes," he pleaded. "I'll shine everyone's shoes. I'll carry the cases, fetch water, and clean the bus. And when we reach the city, I'll look for work, and when I've earned enough, I'll pay you back for the bus-ride. And if you like, you can keep the lamb!"

The last was a tremendous offer. But anything was better than their neighbour's knife.

"You can take it with you!" cried Steffos. "You can take it back to your own country," he rattled on desperately. "Then it can graze on all that beautiful green grass that grows there."

The lady from the distant country by the sea listened in amazement to the fiery offer of the little Greek boy. His big black eyes looked at her so imploringly that she nearly gave in. "No, Steffos," she said gently, "what can't be done, can't be done. You'll have to make the best of it. We must be going soon. The best of luck to you." And away she went.

Steffos felt very unhappy. Bending down he laid his hand on the woolly fleece of the sleeping lamb, as he sadly watched the professor go.

"We are dopes," he said, "a couple of dopes, who cannot even find a way . . ."

Find a way? But what did he see there?

He was looking straight into a big black hole in the side of the bus. The compartment where all the bags and cases were kept. Couldn't he hide in there? With luck, with just the tiniest bit of luck, he could do it easily. Oh, surely heaven would not allow such a small innocent lamb to be slaughtered.

Once again Steffos strolled towards the bus with the lamb over his shoulders. This time the driver did not see him, for he was smoking a cigarette in the shade of the other side. The foreigners were all occupied or out of sight of the bus. Nobody – nobody at all – was paying any attention to Steffos.

It was his big chance. Quickly he cast a final glance around him. Then, sliding the wriggling lamb off his shoulders, he pushed it into the luggage compartment and crawled in after it. It only

took him a few seconds to heave the cases forward, creep in behind them and rearrange them in front of him again.

Steffos was out of breath. He had moved fast, but it had made great demands on his strength. The lamb was playing up, too. It had to be calmed down.

"Be quiet, stupid," he whispered breathlessly. "If they see or hear us, the game's up."

But the lamb baaed again. Just as it had done when it had been caught in the cleft. Steffos hugged the little animal to him and pushed its muzzle under his arm. His own face he thrust into its coat.

The lamb was shivering with fright. It was not the only one, Steffos was trembling too.

"Quiet now, quiet now," he hushed both himself and the baby lamb.

He was panting less now. His heart was not thumping as much either. Gently he rocked the lamb to and fro in the tiny dark space. What would it be like when the door of the compartment was closed, he wondered. Then it would be even smaller and darker.

"We'll just have to grin and bear it, lambo," he whispered. "We have to travel like thieves in the night."

He heard footsteps and voices approaching. Bang, the door slammed to. Inside it was pitch-black. The engine started up. Steffos heard loud thumps above his head. The passengers were climbing into their seats. The whole bus shook.

A sudden jolt and they were off. It was a bad road they were driving over and Steffos bumped his head three times. He almost began to wish he had stayed at home. But he clenched his teeth and stroked the lamb's woolly back. The little thing began to lick him, first on his neck, then on his face. Steffos grinned in the dark.

"Nice and salty, eh," he whispered.

The lamb went on licking with its little rough tongue.

The bus shook and roared. Stones flew up and hit underneath. Feet still shuffled about above Steffos's head, but not as loudly as at first. Then they drove through a pothole and Steffos bumped his head for the fourth time. His eyes watered. He moaned and pressed his face into the lamb's fleece to stifle a cry. It was a difficult journey.

And it took a long, long time.

It grew very stuffy in the tiny compartment.

Steffos could hardly draw breath.

When the bus came to a stop — after hours and hours — he felt like calling out and pounding against the door. But he did not do so. His legs had gone to sleep and his head and back ached terribly. How much longer would it take?

He no longer knew whether it was day or night. He sat with his eyes closed and drowsed just like the little Easter lamb. When the bus finally stopped, Steffos did not even realize it. There was a lot of noise around him, but he did not hear it. The luggage compartment was opened, and suitcases were lifted out. Fresh air came in. Someone shone a torch inside.

"Well, I never," somebody exclaimed.

"It's that rascal of a boy!" the driver stormed. "And with his lamb too! That beast is now the bus-company's property. It will go to the butcher's tomorrow."

Steffos was dragged out and the lamb lifted out of his arms. It struggled wildly, but a moment later it stood with trembling legs on a city pavement.

Then a man's voice said in Dutch: "Well, that certainly takes the cake — and the bun and the biscuit too!"

But Steffos was too far gone to catch any of this.

What happened to Steffos and his lamb after this was even more miraculous than what had gone before. Steffos, waking up in a big strange bed, and Dilemachos, who had come to find his brother, listened to the little professor. And do you know what the result of it was? That they made a trip by train the next day. Then they had to walk three hours to their village, but they did not mind that as they had plenty to talk about. First, that Dilemachos had been offered a job in the hotel where the foreigners were staying. Secondly, that the professor had insisted on paying for the leg-doctor for their mother. Thirdly, that the king's castle would be dug up, but not this year, and that there would then be enough work for all the men in the village. Fourthly, that Steffos had performed an invaluable service to scholarship — the professor who was a man had said that too. Fifthly, that the Easter lamb had been saved by Steffos's professor and would travel with the foreigners to that small, far-away country in the north where such delicious green grass grew.

So, if one fine day you are in Holland and you see in a meadow a very beautiful ram with curly horns, a black nose and amber-coloured eyes, it will most likely be Steffos Mandaki's Easter lamb. For in the two years that have passed since the events related here, it will have grown into a handsome animal.

MAGNUS AND THE SQUIRREL

From the book of the same title

By HANS PETERSON

This story comes from Sweden. Magnus lives a lonely life in a big block of flats. His chief friend is Matthew, a much older boy but one who loves and understands young boys and animals. It is he who asks Magnus to look after a baby squirrel, Jimjim. They are soon inseparable; but inevitably the squirrel grows up, and Magnus has to face up to heart-breaking problems.

A small baby squirrel that stays in a cage at night, and can be allowed to run around in the kitchen during the day, is no trouble at all – as long as he's no bigger than a mouse. But an almost full-grown squirrel, who isn't still for one moment but scuttles around all day, is much more difficult to keep track of. You never know where that kind of squirrel is.

You may be sitting peacefully on the sofa, reading a book, and – ouch! – there's a thump on your head and the squirrel is perched there, clutching your hair with his claws.

109

Or perhaps you're sitting quietly with a glass of lemonade and a couple of newly baked buns, thinking how pleasant it is that it's summer, and so lovely and warm. You wriggle your toes underneath the table and, without warning, something nips them so sharply that you yelp with pain. Or you hear a thud, and before you can bat an eyelid the whole glassful of lemonade has toppled over, the buns are bouncing all over the table, and in the middle of the mess sits a squirrel, making pleased noises as if he had done something really wonderful.

That's the way it was with Jimjim. Magnus's mother was beginning to think he was a frightful nuisance, and she told Matthew so one day when he was having dinner with them.

"I'm afraid you'll have to take Jimjim home with you one of these days, for I really can't keep him any longer," she said. "When is your mother coming home from the hospital?"

"Tomorrow or the day after," said Matthew.

"I wonder if it's a good idea to take a squirrel like Jimjim home to somebody just out of the hospital," said Magnus's father. "I almost think it would be better to let him loose in Slotts Park and let him take care of himself."

"May I say what I think?" said Magnus.

"We know what you think," said his mother. "You think he should stay here."

"Exactly," said Magnus. "You guessed it."

"And what about my curtains and the furniture? And the carpets? What do you think will become of them if Jimjim stays?"

"Well, I for one think it's nicer *without* curtains," said Magnus solemnly. "If you have to chose between Jimjim and curtains, then I think it would be a better idea to take the *curtains* to the park and let them take care of themselves."

"I wonder what Jimjim thinks," said his father. "It's a pity we can't ask him."

"I'll ask," said Magnus. "Jimjim, where are you?"

They all began to search everywhere, underneath the chairs and the table, behind window curtains, and even up around the ceiling. Suddenly they heard a crash from the living room.

"I believe that was a flower pot falling," said Magnus's mother. "One got broken yesterday too. And last week it was a vase."

"Perhaps it's windy outside," said Magnus.

"I think it's Jimjim," said his father.

At that moment Jimjim came hopping into the kitchen. He stopped and clucked as if wanting to explain that he, for one, had nothing whatsoever to do with flower pots.

"Come here, Jimjim!" called Magnus.

But it was Matthew who coaxed Jimjim over with a biscuit and took him in his lap. "Look here, Jimjim," he said. "Do you want to stay here, or do you want to go to Slotts Park and play with other squirrels and lead a normal life?"

"Little Jimjim, surely you would rather stay with me?" Magnus asked. But Jimjim didn't answer. He nibbled at his biscuit, looking at the others now and then, as if he were wondering what all the talk was about.

"Besides, we're going away on holiday next week," said Magnus's father.

"And when you come back from your holiday," said Matthew to Magnus, "it would be lots of fun if you would come out and stay with me for a while before school starts. Of course, we only have a dog and a cat, but the farm next to ours has lambs, and

111

small calves, and other animals. And we could go swimming every day, because I'd be on holiday then too."

Magnus nodded. He didn't want to make a fuss. When his parents and Matthew all thought the same, it didn't matter very much what he said. And perhaps they were right. It certainly was a little difficult keeping a squirrel at home.

"All right, we can ride to Slotts Park with him," he said. "But if Jimjim doesn't want to stay, and follows us when we leave, then I think he should be allowed to stay with us, because then I'll be sure he really wants to. He mustn't come back even if we call him. No matter how loudly I call him, he mustn't come back. Because if he comes, it means he wants to stay with me."

Magnus looked at his mother and father. He thought he had been quite clever, because Jimjim always came when you called him. And if they went to Slotts Park and called Jimjim, and if Jimjim came to him, then they would have to give in and let Jimjim stay with him.

"All right, we'll leave it at that," said his father. "But you must promise to count to fifty twice, before calling Jimjim after you've let him go."

"Why?" said Magnus.

"So he'll have a little time to get used to things first, like climbing trees and jumping from one branch to another and meeting other squirrels... Then you can call."

"Anyhow, we won't go to the park until this evening," said Matthew. "I'll come and get you when I'm through for the day. It stays light so late now that we can stay there for several hours."

"Let's wait till tomorrow," said Magnus.

"Tomorrow I've got to go straight home and tidy up the house before Mother comes back," said Matthew. "My father has such a lot of work just now that he can't manage all the cleaning by himself. We'll go to the park this evening." There was nothing that Magnus could say to that. He picked up Jimjim, fastened on his strap and chain, and followed Matthew down the stairs.

The rain was still falling in the evening, and it was even more miserable than it had been during the day. Matthew was wearing both his leather jacket and his boots and Magnus put his raincoat on. The motorcycle whooshed through puddles of rain water all the way to Slotts Park.

"Everybody should stay indoors in weather like this," said Magnus, when they had parked the motorcycle and were going into the big park.

"We won't stay here long," said Matthew.

"I think we should have waited till a nice day, for Jimjim's sake," said Magnus. "He isn't used to being out-of-doors in the rain."

"There aren't so many people about when it's raining," said Matthew, "so he'll be left more in peace. Besides, I don't think animals care whether it's raining or not."

"I'm sure Jimjim does," said Magnus. "He doesn't like getting wet one bit. I'm sure he'd rather stay at home with me, waiting for nice weather."

Magnus stopped and looked pleadingly at Matthew. Matthew smiled and put his hand on Magnus's shoulder. "There's no need to be so glum, Magnus," he said. "You've had a wonderful time with Jimjim for a whole month. Now that's over and another good time is starting, with holidays and all sorts of nice things to look forward to. Life's like that, and there isn't a thing we can do about it. I know it's hard. But you'll forget about it. Life is like that," Matthew repeated. "Sometimes you wish you could stay young all the time and never grow up. You wish you could play with squirrels and always stay in the first form at school. And sometimes you wish the time would go much faster so that you would soon be as old as the big boys. Sometimes you want one thing, sometimes another. The most difficult time is when you want both things at once."

Magnus didn't quite understand what Matthew was talking about, he sounded so miserable and unhappy that Magnus took his hand.

"But it's nice that you're older than me so I can have you for my big brother," he said.

"Yes, of course. I had nearly forgotten," said Matthew. "A good thing you reminded me."

Matthew had been carrying Jimjim inside his jacket, but as soon as they got into the park, Magnus took the strap and the little chain out of his pocket. Matthew fastened the strap around Jimjim, and the two boys walked slowly across the grass with Jimjim hopping alongside. It was raining heavily now and the air was sweet with the smell of wet grass. Jimjim made cross little noises and stopped every little while to shake himself, as if he didn't like having to hop through wet grass. When Magnus and Matthew stopped under a big oak tree, he scampered up the trunk at once, sat down on a branch, and began to lick his wet fur. But when Magnus called him gently, he came back and sat on his shoulder.

The boys went on towards the hill and the wilder part of the park. Here there were rocks, and thickets of shrubs and trees all

tangled together like a jungle. Magnus was wondering, as they walked on, whether Jimjim would come back when he called once they had let him loose. He was fairly sure he would. But, of course, he couldn't be altogether sure.

"How much farther are we going?" Magnus asked.

"We can stop right here," said Matthew. "But remember, you must count to fifty twice before you call Jimjim."

"By the time I count to fifty twice, Jimjim will be able to run several miles," said Magnus.

"If he runs several miles away from you, then it means he wants to be free," said Matthew.

Magnus sighed and took the strap from around Jimjim's stomach. At first the squirrel didn't seem to notice that he was free. Cautiously he jumped around Magnus's and Matthew's feet. Then he took a series of little leaps along the path, clucking as he went.

"You can borrow my watch," said Matthew. "The second hand goes around twice in about the same time it would take for you to count fifty twice."

Magnus took the watch. The second hand was pointing straight up. He watched it carefully as it moved slowly around and pointed to the right. Magnus looked up to see where Jimjim had gone to.

The squirrel sat still on the path for a few seconds, as if he were planning what he would do. Then he went jumping over to a tree. Magnus and Matthew heard a scratching, rattling noise, and suddenly Jimjim peered down at them from a branch up. He made happy little noises as he climbed farther and farther out on the branch. Then he took an elegant leap over to the next tree.

"You see, he can jump as well as the other squirrels, even though he has never done it before," said Matthew. "This is a normal life for a squirrel."

Magnus didn't say anything, but looked at the watch again. Half a minute had gone by. They heard Jimjim clucking in the treetop and Magnus almost called to him, but Matthew touched his arm and Magnus controlled himself.

The rain was stopping, but the trees and bushes were still dripping. When the second hand pointed straight up again, they heard Jimjim come dashing down a tree. He bounded over to them, and Magnus bent down and stretched out his hand. But Jimjim turned around and jumped away again. He disappeared among some bushes and a moment later they saw his fluffy red tail high up among the branches of a birch tree.

When the second hand pointed straight down once more Magnus couldn't wait any longer. "Jimjim, come here!" he called and made the usual little clucking sound to coax Jimjim back.

Jimjim clucked too, and they heard him climb down the tree. Then there was a rustle, and there was Jimjim farther down the path, sitting looking at them with his tail curled up over his back. He began to nibble at something he was holding between his paws.

"Come here, Jimjim! Come here to me!" called Magnus.

Just then two other squirrels came bounding across the path. They stopped and sniffed at Jimjim, and then one chased the other up the trunk of an old oak tree. Jimjim stared after them. The next moment he too was racing up the tree. The chattering of the three squirrels sounded from farther and farther away.

Magnus and Matthew both called Jimjim. They clucked and coaxed, and walked back and forth on the path for a long while. But Jimjim never came.

"He wants to be free," said Magnus glumly.

"Yes, and it's really best for him," said Matthew. "Besides, in a few days you're all going away on holiday, aren't you?"

Magnus tried to answer, but his voice wouldn't come. They walked slowly through the park, back to the motorcycle. Now the setting sun was beginning to break the clouds and the air felt dry and warm again. Magnus climbed up behind Matthew on the motorcycle, and with a roar they were off down the street. They didn't go straight home, but made a little detour round by the harbour, where they looked at all the boats. And by the time they got home, Magnus felt much more cheerful.

A few days later, just before Magnus was to go away on holiday with his mother and father, he and Matthew rode to Slotts Park once more. They walked around, searching and calling, but Jimjim didn't come, and Magnus never saw him again. He sometimes saw other squirrels, of course, and some of them looked very much like Jimjim, but not one of them was the real Jimjim.

Jimjim probably found a hole in a tree and lived there the whole winter with a good supply of nuts. The following summer he doubtless found a wife and had lots of children. And by then he had probably forgotten about Magnus and Matthew and the time he was their pet. That's the worst of squirrels, they have hardly any memory at all.

ZERO, THE CAPTAIN'S DOG

From the book "The Captain's Dog"

By LOUIS ENAULT

Twice in a week, the shaggy little dog, Zero, nearly lost his life in the French port of Honfleur, trying to swim after a sailor who had forgotten him. Both times it was Captain Pigault who rescued him from drowning. Zero became the captain's loyal companion – until the captain married and Madame Pigault saw Zero as a rival. When Zero made the mistake of gobbling new-laid eggs, Madame told her husband the dog must go. Without a word, Captain Pigault took Zero to a friend, Captain Tautin, setting sail for Senegal, and gave him to this kind man. As Pigault left the ship, Zero howled after him. The story here takes up as Captain Pigault returns home to his wife, and the housekeeper, good-natured, fat Jeannette.

"I have sent Zero away," said the captain to his wife, in a tone of judicial severity. "The house is now rid of this source of annoyance, and to-morrow you can have fresh eggs for breakfast – if the hens will lay them. You certainly cannot complain of the law's delay in disposing of the criminal."

Delighted with her victory, Madame Pigault was amiable in the extreme. The captain was inclined to meet her half way, but it must be confessed that he was not very successful in maintaining his share of the conversation. While he listened to his wife, Zero's cry kept sounding in his ears and distracted his attention. Every little thing called up the memory of the lost. When the kitchen door was opened, and the captain saw that Zero was not in his usual place, his heart sank within him. The dog's name was constantly on his lips, but never uttered.

Now, Madame Pigault was not a bad woman, in spite of her faults; she loved her husband sincerely, and she could not fail to see that he was troubled. At first she was angry to think that he should mourn so over a dog, when he had a wife to console him; but he did not cease his careful attention to her welfare or neglect the courtesy he always showed her, and as the days went on and his grief did not seem to diminish, she felt something like remorse, and realized that she had deprived him of a very dear friend.

The captain was quick to discern the change, and the pleasure of finding his wife in so considerate a mood was sometimes great enough to banish all thought of Zero. But this was only at rare moments; memory soon revived, and the captain would once more try to imagine where the dog was, if he were well treated, if he were unhappy, if – oh, reader, do not laugh – if he still thought of his master. The captain sought in vain to conceal these painful reveries from his wife; his thoughts were painted upon his face. She, to spare her husband's grief, never spoke of Zero, but, strange as it may appear, the dog was almost constantly in her mind.

"In six months," the captain said to himself, "I shall go to Cherbourg to make up my accounts; then I'll land at Isigny and run out to Grandcamp and – see him once more."

Meanwhile, the captain looked eagerly for the letter which Tautin had promised to send when he got into port. And one memorable day, just after breakfast-time, it came! The captain was not obliged to look twice at the bold superscription to recognize Tautin's handwriting, and the postmark told that the ship had reached her destination. He put the letter in his pocket, feeling that when he read it he must be alone. Madame Pigault was not aware of the postman's visit. The captain conversed with her for a few moments on indifferent topics, then, in accordance with his custom after meals, lighted his pipe and went outside to smoke. Halfway down the hill he went, through the opening among the trees, and seated himself on a moss-covered rock in full view of the sea. He took out the letter and opened it with feverish haste. Tautin, who was not an accomplished scholar, wrote as follows:

St. Louis, Senegal, May 12, 1878.

"Dear Old Chap, – I take my pen in hand to write you a few words as I promised. As you know, letters are not in my line except to the old woman, and then not often, and most of my writing is done in the log-book. But a promise is a promise, so here goes!

"First, then, you must know that as long as we were in the channel and Zero could still smell the coast of Normandy, he kept on crying, howling, whining, and lamenting in a way that even made the sailors pity him. Hoping to get him quiet, I sent him his dinner when the men had theirs, but he would not eat or drink. At dusk he calmed down a little, probably because he hadn't any more noise left in him, and when I saw that the music had stopped, I went down the ladder to talk to him about you. I am sure he understood me, for when I spoke your name he turned up his eyes and wagged his tail, which is a certain sign.

"When I went up, I left the scuttle open to give him air. He leaped through like an india-rubber fiend, slipped out of my hands, ran between my legs, and got loose before I knew he was there. He ran across the deck three or four times as if he had gone mad, and I was afraid he would jump overboard. He was evidently looking for you, and not finding you he rushed to and fro as if he was crazy, knocking against everyone who got in his track. Finally, they cornered him and got a line hitched to his collar, and turned him over to the cabin-boy and I told him to slack up a little, but the fellow pulled so that the boy had to double over backwards and lay hold of the rigging to hold himself upright. Well, we let him have his way, and watched to see what he would do.

"The wind was aft and we were making about twelve knots, heading straight out to sea. But the rascal knew the points of the compass. He made like a shot for the stern, rose up on his hind legs, put his paws on the rail, pointed his nose towards shore, although it was now out of sight, and sniffed the air that came from home. The sea got rough, and some water came on board, wetting him to the skin. We tried to call him, but he would pay no attention

123

to us. It was no use to drag him away; he went straight back again, with plaintive yelps that seemed to say that he knew his place and would stick to it whatever happened.

"When we got into the Gulf of Gascony and began to toss about a bit, he seemed to realize that watching was no use and that you couldn't walk out on the water to find him. Besides, we had tacked so many times that he probably lost his bearings and would have found it difficult to keep his nose towards Honfleur, even if we had given him a chart! He left his post, and lay down at the foot of the mainmast with your handkerchief to his mouth, as if he would still have something of yours about him. When one of the ship's boys tried to take the rag away, he made as if he would tear him to pieces. After that he was quiet and said nothing to nobody.

"My men took on the poor fellow and did all they could to comfort him. If he had eaten everything they offered him, he would have been dead of indigestion in a week; but it was grief, not gluttony, that was likely to kill him. He evidently knew what was good for him, and instead of gorging himself with food and drink, as a good many people would have done under the circumstances, he ate only enough to sustain life. He saw that everyone tried to be good to him, but, without being disdainful, he made no show of thanks. He permitted caresses, but did not return them, although it was clear that he liked to be caressed. The sailors told one another that this dog had the heart of a Christian. He will be long remembered on board the *Alix*.

"Well, we got to St. Louis without any mishaps, and with the crew in good condition. Zero was inclined to be dull during the latter portion of the voyage. He slept much of the time, and often barked in his sleep, which shows that he was dreaming. He was glad enough to get on shore, and after two or three jumps, he began to fly around with his nose to the ground, as if hunting for someone's trail. I tell you this only because it is true. How that dog loves you!

"But stranger still was to come. He inspected, one after another, at least ten different vessels lying at the docks, and smelled of everybody on board. He looked for you everywhere, and, finally, convinced that you were not to be found, came back to the *Alix* for his rations and to rest a little. Then he began the search over again.

"You know what tongue-waggers sailors are when they get ashore. Mine are like all the rest. In a few days, Zero's story was all over the place, and your dog was the object of general attention. An English captain offered a big price for him, and would have doubled it, if I had been disposed to haggle. He says if the dog ever belongs to him, he will treat him like a dear friend, and when he dies put a monument over his grave, with an inscription in French and English.

"'In Dutch, too,' I said, 'if you want him to understand it. Dutch is his native language and he never spoke anything else.'

"But all this talk made me uneasy. Sailors, like soldiers, are not always particular about ownership, and among all these fellows of different nationalities I was afraid there might be some who might appropriate the dog without saying, by your leave. I have done the best I can. I have taken Zero to a tavern back in the middle of the town – the 'Two Poles' – you know the place; many's the good dinner we've had together there; – and as the landlord's dog, a big Danish hound, is dead, Zero had his vacant kennel. I chain him when I go out, and when I am at the hotel he stays in my room and seems to be contented. But he is such a rogue that he may slip out of his collar. He can do anything with his paws, just like a monkey.

We are good friends, because he is a discerning animal, and knows that I am fond of him. But you need not be jealous. I can see that no one takes your place in his affections. Sometimes he looks at me as if asking news of you. Not having any, of course, I can tell him nothing of your present welfare; but I frequently talk of you, and that always seems to give him pleasure.

"I have disposed of my cargo on first-rate terms, and since I don't want to go home in ballast, I have got my eye out for some freight with which I think I can do well – dyewoods for Caen and Cherbourg. That would suit me, because it would take me near home and end my seafaring. My rheumatism warns me that it is time to forsake the briny. If everything goes as I hope, I shall be in Grandcamp in two months. Then you can come and see your dog and your friend,

Jacques Tautin

"P. S. – Here's a pretty piece of business! I wrote this letter day before yesterday, to be sure and have it ready for the post, which leaves tonight. Today I came back to the hotel and went to look for Zero – no Zero to be found! No one has seen him, no one knows anything about him. The hotel attendants can give me no information as to what has become of him. I hurried down to the ship. Zero was not there – had not been there. But the cabin-boy, who is an observing lad for his size, says that he saw the beast going towards the outer port. I went there to see if I could get trace of him. I came across Anzoufe, an old friend, who is surveyor here, and who has been often on board the *Alix* and therefore knows Zero. He saw the dog following a sailor belonging to the *Two Friends*, a sloop from Dieppe, Captain Franqueville, which made three voyages to Honfleur last year, and was now on the point of clearing for Marseilles. Zero, it seems, followed the sailor as if he had found a master. That gave me a turn. If it was the Dutchman, Zero's former owner, we shall never set eyes on the dog again. I started off to get a word with Franqueville. It never rains but it pours; the sloop had been gone for an hour, bound, they told me, for Marseilles with freight for Cadiz and Gibraltar. I am good deal upset by this mischance, for I had learned to be fond of the wretch. Well, you are rid of him, at any rate: that's the main thing. I am sorry if I have not taken proper care of him, but I did the best I knew how."

"J. T."

Captain Pigault, having devoured the letter with all possible speed, went over it once more, slowly, phrase by phrase, line by line, almost word by word. Then he let it fall upon his knees, shook his head two or three times, and muttered to himself:

"I might have known, when I turned him away from the house, that the affair would end this way."

Someone was coming, brushing against the leaves, and pushing aside the branches that intercepted the path. He turned, and found himself face to face with his wife.

"Is it you?" he asked, gently.

"From whom is your letter?" the pretty creature demanded, frowning slightly as she spoke.

"From Zero," replied the captain, absorbed in thought.

"Ah! Zero has learned to write, then?" madame responded, with a shrug of her shoulders.

"That is to say, from Captain Tautin, to whom I gave the dog."

"And who sends you news of him?"

"Yes! But what brings you out here?"

"That is easily explained," said madame, whose mood had suddenly softened. She seated herself beside her husband and continued. "You went out this morning a little sooner than usual; you walked away rapidly with a preoccupied air; I was afraid something had gone wrong, and I came to see what was the matter."

"It's no great matter," replied the captain, drily, "Tautin has lost Zero; that's all."

Lise wanted to say that, as long as the dog was gone, it made no difference who had him, but her husband's evident displeasure awed her into silence. She took up the letter and read it through in an undertone.

"It is very unfortunate," she said, feeling moved in spite of herself. "Who could have foreseen such a thing?"

"We never foresee anything," the captain replied, sadly.

The months went by, and the foliage about White Rock Villa began to display autumnal tints. No event had occurred to disturb the calm monotony of the life led by Lise and the captain. Zero's name was never spoken by either of them. If the captain had any sorrowful reflections about what had happened, he was discreet enough

128

to keep them to himself, and Lise, as if to atone for the suffering she had unwittingly caused, was a gentle and devoted wife. She seemed to have undergone a moral conversion. Her husband's wish became her law. The captain had lost his dog, but he had found his wife, and realizing this he was not devoid of appreciation. Sometimes, however, he fell to wondering what had become of Zero, and then a shadow gathered upon his brow. He sought to drive such thoughts out of his mind; he regarded them as the manifestations of an unmanly sentiment. Lise felt what was going on in his mind in these moments, and she was sad in sympathy.

She did not neglect her household duties, and there was not in all Honfleur a better managed house than hers. By careful economy, and a judicious expenditure of the resources at her command, she provided much that many wealthier people regarded as beyond their means. Fortunately, all men are not indifferent to the merits of a diligent housewife. Lise took advantage of every opportunity to obtain the best she could get for her well-appointed table. On market days she rose at dawn, and followed by Jeannette carrying the basket, she made her bargains with the peasants, selecting her purchases with the utmost care.

Now, on a certain Saturday, as the two were returning with their usual load of delicacies, and talking about the fine dishes they would prepare for the still sleeping captain, Lise, walking in advance, saw crouching before the door a strange form, whose purport she was not at first glance able to distinguish. It was a dark mass of skin and hair, and did not move. She drew back, in answer to that instinct of fear at the unknown, always quickly felt in the feminine breast, and called out, "Jeannette, Jeannette! What *can* that be? – Look! – there!"

Jeannette, strong of nerves, advanced and touched the unknown object inquiringly with her foot. A plaintive murmur, too weak to be a groan, came from the prostrate thing. Then, slowly and painfully, it rose, displayed its outline, and the two women beheld before them – a dog!

"Great heavens, madame," cried Jeannette, nearly losing her hold upon the basket of provisions, in the excitement of the moment. "Great heavens, it's Zero!"

Zero, for in truth it was he, wagged his tail gently on hearing his name, as if in acknowledgment of Jeannette's salutation. But his eyes now fell upon Madame Pigault, and remembering that she loved him not, he let his tail fall, drew down his ears, and, with a glance that demanded pity, he dragged himself to the other side of the walk, and lay with his gaze fixed upon the threshold, which perhaps he would never cross again, but to which he had returned to die.

"Ah, madame," said the compassionate Jeannette, "see how thin he is. His bones almost stick through his skin!"

"Yes," replied Lise, "he must have suffered a great deal. I never supposed a sight like this would move me so."

The sight of the poor unhappy creature was in fact more powerful than words. It entered into her heart, and awakened a feeling of remorse.

"How badly I must have treated him," she thought, "to make him so afraid of me."

She called to him. Zero arose as if to go to her; then, thinking she could not be in earnest, he lay down once more in the same place. The young woman understood, and said affectionately, "Well, if you won't come to me, I will go to you."

She crossed the path, while Zero cowered in fear; but she, to reassure him took the rough battered head into her two hands, stroked it, caressed it, and called him by all the sweet names she could remember – she, from whom he had hitherto received only rebuffs and disdain.

The transformation was so complete that Zero, with his first bitter experience of life, could not believe it to be genuine. He looked at his mistress as if to make sure that he was not deceived. Little by little he was convinced, and he began to lick her hands, and to look his thanks with his large, clear, expressive eyes.

Meanwhile, Jeannette had opened the kitchen door, and Zero was seized with an intense desire to follow her, but he lay still and looked at the paradise from which he had been so ruthlessly exiled.

"Come," said Lise, divining his thoughts.

She entered and he followed, but he was so exhausted by hunger and fatigue that he dropped upon the floor, as if able to go no further.

"He's starving," cried Jeannette. Lise took the loaf and cut a thick slice of bread, which she divided into three pieces and fed to him. He made a mouthful of each piece, and would have devoured the remainder of the loaf if Jeannette had not interfered.

"You've given him enough to begin with, madame," said the prudent Jeannette. "He must not eat too much after being so long without food. I'll make him some soup by and by."

Meanwhile, Zero, his hunger appeased, began to pluck up courage and looked about him. He smelled out the captain's coat, which Jeannette the night before had placed on a chair near the fireplace, and was certain that his master could not be far off. He looked first at Lise and then at the stairway leading to the captain's chambers. It was plain enough what his wishes were.

"Ah, madame," said Jeannette, clasping her hands, "how happy the Captain will be to have Zero back once more!"

"Yes, yes, and we must not delay his pleasure any longer. Go up softly and open the chamber door. Zero shall wake him."

Zero listened attentively to this dialogue and seemed to comprehend its purport. He followed Jeannette quietly till she opened the chamber door, whereupon he sprang forward, got entangled in her skirts, nearly threw her down, then freed himself in some way, dashed into the room, leaped toward the bed, and alighted on the chest of his sleeping master.

132

Never was a man more rudely awakened. The captain uttered forcible ejaculations before realizing what had happened; and the dog, fearing he had done some mischief, jumped to the floor. The captain looked, and seeing the animal there thought himself dreaming. But Zero sprang a second time upon the bed and there was no doubt as to the reality of his presence. What other dog would ever display such irrepressible joy at sight of this master from whom he had so long been separated? The captain buried his fingers in Zero's shaggy coat, and gazed into the creature's eyes.

"Well," he said finally, "you're no handsomer than before, but you seem to be just as good. How on earth did you get here?"

Zero would unquestionably have responded to this inquiry, if the captain had ever taken the trouble to teach him French, but as his native language was Dutch, he could not.

Lisa now entered, smiling, displaying sincere enjoyment at her husband's pleasure. The captain, on seeing her, realized that Zero had left sundry dirty marks upon the coverlet.

"Get down, you rascal," he said gently, grasping the animal by the nape of the neck, "you forgot to take your bath this morning."

"Oh, let him stay," exclaimed Lise. "You two are so happy that it is worth a little extra laundry to see you together."

The speech was so entirely at variance with the young woman's former treatment of Zero that the captain stared in astonishment. Lise understood, and spoke again. "I found him, and I sent him to you," she said. "Don't think any more about the past. I hope now that we shall be very happy – all three of us."

"All three of us?" demanded the captain, scarcely able to believe his ears.

"Yes, all three of us," repeated Lise, firmly. "I have been too hard upon the poor fellow," she went on, placing her hand on Zero's head. "But you must not judge me too severely. It was because you made so much of him... Now that he is back, you may be certain that I shall never make any trouble on his account. I would like him to be fond of me. Do you think he will?"

134

"He will adore you. I am sure of it," said the captain laughingly. "*I* shall be the jealous one now."

Zero soon regained his lost strength, and his gentleness, affection and intelligence were the constant delight of the husband and wife. He showed a preference for madame's society, but often he glanced at the captain with a knowing air, which seemed to say, "Of course you know I like you best, but we must flatter the ladies a little!"

The captain approved of his dog's wisdom and never made any complaint.

TOO MANY KITTENS

From the book of the same title

By HELEN HOKE

This pleasant little story of a small girl's embarrassment of riches-too many kittens to manage-really happened to the author, with a few differences of circumstance, the summer she was eight. But, alas, unlike Suzy of the story, Helen was not allowed to keep more than one of the furry little charmers. Her mother, an understanding woman but a busy one, viewed a whole family of kittens coming into her big househould as-well, *too many kittens*. Some thirty years later, remembering the episode, Helen found it fun to write about in a picture book.

If anyone had told Suzy she would wish sometime that she were *not* at Sea Acres, she would not have believed it. But that was just what she was wishing this very minute. And it was all on account of Ginger's new kittens. Here they were, five furry little balls curled up in a basket in the back pantry, and Ginger looking at them with round, proud eyes.

But they couldn't stay!

"If it were any place but Sea Acres," Suzy's mother had said, shaking her head, the sunny May morning they were born.

"Oh, but I want them so much!" Suzy begged.

"But will the *boarders* want them?" sighed Suzy's mother. "This place already has too many people in it, to have pets also."

Suzy had to admit this was true – it certainly *was* a busy household. And, also, somehow Suzy could not imagine Mr. Hodge or the Judge or Miss Crockett or any of The Regulars playing with five furry kittens, or being glad to have them chasing around underfoot.

"You'll just have to promise me you'll give them away as soon as they can walk," said Suzy's mother.

So Suzy promised. There wasn't anything else she could do.

Suzy knew all about what Miss Crockett and the Judge thought of animals. But after Ginger's kittens came, she didn't want to think about it. And every time she went out on the back porch, they looked cuter than ever. And they *were* cute, no doubt about it.

They were adorable! Well, she would just have to plan some way to keep them after they got to running around. But no matter how hard she thought, she couldn't think up even one little bit of a plan.

At last a day came when Suzy knew she must keep her promise. For her mother had said that as soon as the kittens could walk, they must be given away!

Out on the back porch, Suzy watched them wobble clumsily across the floor. They were walking - they really were!

Suzy had always thought Sea Acres the most wonderful place in the world. Every spring, she could hardly wait until time to open the big rambling house and repaint the sign that said: SEA ACRES   ROOM AND BOARD   Sam Smiley, Proprietor

Sam Smiley was Suzy's father and he ran such a good boarding house that the same people came back year after year. The people who came back every year were called The Regulars. The Regulars said that Suzy's mother baked the most delicious cherry pies in the country. And they told all their friends that they got more for their money at Sea Acres because FISHING was included.

FISHING was Uncle Tim's department. He had an old boat called *Lulu Belle*. And plenty of fishing rods. And he furnished the bait FREE. Of course the bait was only worms that he dug on the beach. And of course if the guests caught any fish, they ate them for supper, which helped save on the meat bill. But just the same, FISHING was one of the biggest attractions at Sea Acres.

But kittens weren't. Kittens weren't the least bit an attraction. And Suzy knew it. She could just see Miss Crockett's face if one of the new kittens got into her knitting. And the Judge always said he couldn't be near animals of any sort because, he said, they made him itch. That was why he didn't mind Ginger. She never went into the front of the house or up on the front porch or even into the front yard. Ginger liked the barn.

Suzy reached down and picked up the little black one that she had named Inky. Inky blinked at her and rubbed against her arm.

"Oh," said Suzy, "I can't give YOU away."

Then she picked up the one with the cute little stripes – Frisky. Then the one with the white patch over his eye – Patches. Then the one with a white bib – Bibsy. Then the very, very tiny one that was yellow all over – Amber. And as she put them back into the basket, one by one, she whispered softly, "I can't give you... or you... or *you*... or YOU away, either."

Ginger watched nervously while all this went on.

"It's almost as if she KNOWS," thought Suzy.

"*Miaou*...," mewed Ginger, anxiously.

That settled it. Suzy hid the kittens in her apron and ran off the back porch, shutting the door just in time to keep Ginger in.

141

Now, what Suzy *thought* she was going to do was not what she did at all. She *thought* she was going to run right down to the village and give away the five kittens: one to Mr. Mitchell, the man who ran the grocery store, one to Billy Bogg, who ran the gas station, one to the Rileys who always had room for one more, and the last two to Mr. Blower, the village fireman, because there were never more than one or two fires a season and he led a lonely life.

But Suzy didn't do this, at all. Because on the way out of the house, she happened to pass the cellar stairs. The door was open, which it hardly ever was, because it wasn't used much, and her mother went down into the cellar only about once a month, when it was time to bring up more jars of jam.

"Oh!" decided Suzy standing stock still, with the kittens in her apron, and looking at the open cellar door. "I'll hide them down there for a little while, until I decide just EXACTLY who I'm going to give them to."

Suzy walked quickly through the door. Then she shut it softly, and looked down. It was pretty dark in the cellar, but there was one very small window that opened into the garden. A little row of flowers grew in front of this small window, so nobody could look in and see the kittens on the floor.

Suzy walked carefully down the cellar stairs. Over by the wall, underneath the window, there was an old wood-basket and a torn blanket that would make a nice, soft bed. Suzy went over to the basket and fluffing up the blanket, put the kittens down on it. At once they cuddled up and went fast asleep.

"If they'll just sleep all the time," Suzy thought, "everything will be all right."

She hurried up the cellar steps, opened the door quietly, and shut it behind her very quietly indeed. Then she breathed a big sigh of relief. There! Everything was all right now.

But it wasn't. Almost *right away*, she began to worry. How was she ever going to *feed* the kittens without telling her mother or the cook what she had done with Ginger's babies?

But she did not have time to worry very long because she heard voices on the front porch, calling, "Suzy, Suzy, come here!"

Suzy ran towards the voices. Outside on the porch, the Judge and Miss Crockett and Mr. Hodge were peering through the living room window.

"Goodness, whatever has happened to Ginger," Mr. Hodge was saying. "She has always been such a well-behaved cat and stayed in the barn, where she belongs. But now look at her – running around your mother's parlor like mad, Suzy. She must be hunting for a mouse."

"A mouse!" squealed Miss Crockett.

"Oh, no," said Suzy, "it isn't a mouse. It's her kittens. We... we had to take them away."

"Kittens!" snorted the Judge. "I didn't know there were any kittens around here."

Suzy's mother came along just in time to say gently, "Yes, Ginger had five kittens, but of course we couldn't let them bother you. So Suzy took charge of them until they were old enough to give away. Poor Ginger! We'll put her back in the barn now. And Suzy and I will do our best to keep her from being a nuisance. But she may keep looking around for them for a few days."

"Just so she doesn't come near ME," said the Judge, "because ALL animals make me *itch*."

Suzy sighed out loud.

"Never mind, dear," said her mother, putting her arm across Suzy's shoulders. "Ginger will forget all about it very soon."

143

And Ginger did, after a while. But Suzy didn't. She couldn't. All day long she had to think up ways of getting milk down to the cellar without anyone seeing her. First, she asked Cook if she could take up Miss Tipton's tea tray. And she suggested that an extra jug of cream would please Miss Tipton very much. But Cook was cross and said that more cream was exactly what Miss Tipton did NOT need. She was fat enough as it was. So Suzy had to give up that plan.

Next, Suzy asked if she could take her glass of milk out on the porch. But her mother looked at her so strangely when she gave her permission that Suzy knew she couldn't try THAT again, either. Next thing she knew, Mother would be asking WHY. And Suzy didn't want to answer that.

Then – to make the problem even worse – the kittens began to enjoy running around so much that Suzy couldn't make them stay in their basket. They played all over the cellar floor. And once she came down to find the little one up on the window sill, trying his best to get through the glass to where the flowers grew outside. And one day Inky even climbed up three steps on the staircase!

There was no doubt about it. The kittens would have to go, unless she could get someone to help her take care of them. But who was there to get? No one. Suzy sat on the cellar steps and cried as if her heart would break.

Who would have dreamed that there *was* a Someone, after all? And that the Someone was the Judge!

It happened like this: when Suzy went up the cellar stairs and opened the door at the top, just after she had burst into tears, she bumped right into the Judge. She knew that she looked very red-nosed and sniffly and she tried her best to hide her face.

But the Judge had very sharp eyes. Looking at her hard, he said, "Why, what's the matter with our Suzy?"

When Suzy heard the kind voice of the Judge, she burst into tears all over again and ran back through the cellar door. When the Judge started after her, Suzy turned around on the top step and sobbed, "Oh, you mustn't... mustn't come down here. You'll ITCH."

"Itch, nothing," said the Judge. "If there's something down here that's making you cry, I want to find out about it." And he walked right past her and down the stairs.

Suzy was afraid to see what she knew was going to happen. With a big sob, she hid her face in her hands. And she didn't look down until she heard the Judge give a little chuckle and say, "Humph! Can you imagine that!"

Then Suzy opened her eyes wide and peered down into the cellar. What the Judge was laughing at was Inky. The little rascal was trying his best to scramble up the Judge's slippery shoe! And he did it, too. In a minute, there Inky was, hanging onto the Judge's shoe laces. Then he climbed right up onto the big, shiny toe, and he pushed his little head against the Judge's ankle and rubbed and rubbed and rubbed.

"Why, he *likes* me," said the Judge, looking very pleased.

"He likes me, too," said Suzy sadly, coming down the steps and walking over beside the Judge and Inky. "That's why I couldn't bear to give him away. But I – I promised my mother I would. And I promised her I'd give all the others away, too. And she thinks I *did*. But what I really did was to hide them down here. And now they're growing up. And they won't stay in their basket. And they're HUNGRY all the time … and… and…" and Suzy burst into tears once more.

"Yes," said the Judge, "I can see it's been quite a problem for you. Let me think…"

Suzy looked at him hopefully, through her tears. The Judge was a wonderful man. Maybe he could think of a way to save the kittens yet!

"If I can just get Mr. Hodge and Miss Crockett and Miss Spencer – and your Uncle Tim –"

"Get them to do *what*?" said Suzy, her eyes shining with exitement.

"Why, hide the kittens for you, of course," said the Judge.

"Ohhhh," said Suzy, "do you think they *would*? But how… where…?"

"Well, those of us who are Regulars each have a little porch off our rooms, haven't we? And we could get boxes that would be covered, and warm enough, for beds for the kittens."

"Yes," said Suzy, "but there's Mary, the maid, who comes in to clean every morning…"

"And we *always* go out on the porch when she cleans… and she NEVER cleans our porches anyhow," said the Judge.

"You mean… you mean you'd each keep a kitten on your porch for me?" said Suzy.

"That's exactly what I mean," declared the Judge. "And that frisky little one over there can go with Uncle Tim and live on his boat. It will be good for him. Keep him company. And you can still visit him whenever you want to and see how the kitten is doing."

"What about Miss Crockett's knitting?" said Suzy, looking worried.

"She knits too much anyhow. She can put it away when she goes out on the porch," said the Judge.

"But... but what about your Itch," said Suzy bravely.

"It's only animals *in* the house that bother me," explained the Judge. "I don't itch when I'm near animals outdoors."

"Oh, I'm so happy," Suzy said. "But how are we going to get the kittens up to the porches without Mother seeing them?"

"Well, you just go upstairs and help your mother set the table. I'll take charge of the whole thing," said the Judge. Then he put his finger to his lips and bent down to Suzy's ear and whispered: "Remember... not a word to anyone!"

"Not a word," promised Suzy, as she scampered up the stairs.

The wonderful thing was that it all happened just the way the Judge planned it. By the next day, all the kittens had porch homes, and Suzy's mother must not have noticed a thing, because she didn't say a word about it.

Inky, of course, had a little box on the Judge's porch. Miss

Crockett seemed to be *very* happy with Amber. Patches went to Miss Spencer. Bibsy went to Mr. Hodge. And Uncle Tim walked off with one coat-pocket-full of the wiggly little striped one, named Frisky.

Frisky seemed very pleased with life on the *Lulu Belle*, Uncle Tim whispered to Suzy next day. "And why shouldn't he be," Uncle Tim went on, "with fish to eat whenever his heart desires?"

As the summer went on, the kittens behaved splendidly on their porches. And Suzy was sure it would have been the nicest summer she had ever had at Sea Acres, if only there weren't so many errands to run, way down to the village.

The Judge would decide that Inky ought to have some catnip.

"Run down and get it, like a good girl, won't you, Suzy?" he would say.

Or Miss Crockett would want a very *special* brand of cat food from the grocery store. Or Miss Spencer would think her Patches should have a rubber mouse to play with. Even Mr. Hodge occasionally sent Suzy places for things for little Bibsy.

All this kept Suzy much busier than she could manage very well.

Then, after a while, another worry turned up: Miss Spencer and Miss Crockett and Mr. Hodge and the Judge were getting so *very* fond of their kittens that Suzy began to wonder if they remembered the kittens *really* belonged to *her*. One by one, she reminded them:

"You know," she said timidly to the Judge, one day, "Inky is just *borrowed.*"

"Certainly, certainly," the Judge sputtered, but Suzy caught him looking very fiercely at her, and very tenderly at Inky.

"Oh dear," she thought, "I wouldn't have gone to all this trouble if I hadn't been sure I could have the kittens back when all the boarders go."

Sometimes Suzy thought that *maybe* her mother had guessed. But she wasn't sure. And nobody ever said the kittens' names out loud at the big dining-room table. Or on the big front porch where everybody sat after dinner. So, officially, it was still a secret.

And most of the time, Suzy felt they had really kept the secret after all. Because Cook, who was a crosspatch, was always going around saying, "Lucky we got rid of them kittens. I'd have certainly given notice if I had had to have them under my feet all summer. Bad enough having Suzy always in the kitchen asking for a glass of milk. Never *saw* such a child for milk — and she used to hate it."

Sometimes Suzy almost wished the kittens *weren't* a secret. That was when Miss Crockett went off for a day and asked her to keep her eye on "you know what." That meant Suzy had to stay around the house. And Mother kept asking why she didn't go out in the fresh air, which was what Suzy very much preferred, herself.

But at last Labor Day was in sight. Labor Day meant packing-up day for the Regulars at Sea Acres. Labor Day meant good-by for another year. And school next day for Suzy. But *this* year, Labor Day meant explaining about the kittens to Mother! Over and over, Suzy told herself that, after all, keeping them had been the Judge's idea – and the Judge was a Regular. But she *had* promised Mother to give the kittens away, and she *hadn't* kept her promise - not really. Oh, dear, how mixed up things could get!

And then, too, Suzy had still another worry: every summer before this, she had been easily able to run enough errands for neighbors and The Regulars, to earn a few dollars for Christmas presents.

(Suzy felt it was very important that Christmas presents be bought with one's *own* money – what kind of Christmas present for Mother or Father would it be, if it were bought with *their* money!) But this summer, what with the many, many trips to the village just for the kittens, Suzy simply couldn't make time for the Christmas-money errands.

"Oh, dear," Suzy thought, "I'll just have to *make* them myself – pot-holders and pen-wipers, or something like that. And I'm really not a bit good at sewing." But the thought of how much fun it would be to take Inky, and Frisky, and Patches, and Bibsy, and Amber back home with her, was some comfort.

At last, Labor Day was there. Suzy woke up with the sun streaming over her and thought, "What a lovely day."

The next minute she thought: "Oh goodness, this is the day that Mother is going to find out about the kittens!"

Just the same, it was going to be wonderful to get into the car with all the trunks packed on top and start for home – with five darling little kittens traveling with her. Maybe – she hadn't quite decided – she should leave Frisky with Uncle Tim to keep him company. Uncle Tim lived all year on *Lulu Belle*. And Frisky was a very *difficult* little kitten to keep track of.

Thinking all these things, Suzy dressed hastily, then rushed down to the dining-room, ready to make the ANNOUNCEMENT.

BUT... it was Mother who made an ANNOUNCEMENT. The most surprising and really AWFUL announcement Suzy could imagine.

"Look, Suzy," said Mother, "Ginger has a surprise for you. And this time you can *keep* the surprise, and take it home – because there aren't any Regulars at home who will mind."

Suzy took one look! There was Ginger lying proudly in the big straw basket that was usually used for a waste-paper basket. And all around her were brand new kittens. Even *more* kittens than the last time. Five... six... SEVEN kittens. Suzy burst into tears.

"Why Suzy," said her mother. "I thought you *liked* kittens."

150

"Ohhhhhhhh," sobbed Suzy, "I do... I do... but not *too many* kittens."

Just then in walked the Judge and Miss Spencer and Mr. Hodge and Miss Crockett, each carrying a kitten to be returned to Suzy before they left.

"Goodness gracious," said Suzy's mother, with twinkling eyes.

"Well, well, well," said her father, and his eyes twinkled, too. "There *are* quite a lot of kittens to go home with us, aren't there?"

Just then the Judge cleared his throat most impressively and said, "Hrrrrumph! If you've got so many... I wouldn't mind taking Inky back to my city apartment. I'm all over my Itch."

"And Miss Spencer and I have talked things over," said Miss Crockett, "and we are even willing to pay Suzy a whole dollar each if she will let *us* keep *our* kittens."

"I was thinking the very same thing," said Mr. Hodge, fumbling in his pocket and bringing out a dollar bill.

"Oh," gasped Suzy, "Oh." And for a minute she couldn't say another word.

Then, because she was so relieved, she ran over to the Judge and hugged him and Inky, both together. And she hugged Miss Crockett and her kitten, and Miss Spencer and hers, and Mr. Hodge and his.

"I never was so happy in my life," she told them all.

The next minute, there Suzy was, with four crisp dollar bills in her pocket for Christmas gifts, and a whole lovely new batch of seven kittens to take home.

It was the best, positively the best, summer she had ever had at Sea Acres!

MELI'S PET HOSPITAL

From the book "Meli"

By SELMA LAGERLÖF

Meli is a lonely little hunchback girl who has lived as much in hospital as in her own home. She is too delicate to play with the other children and her sadness embarrasses people — even her devoted father and the neighbour's big dog. Meli's family live in a little mining town where nothing grows green among the slag heaps and in summer the sun burns up the land. But she loves the heat and has made a cave playroom among the stones that form her garden. Here she cares for her sick dolls.

Now, Meli had already attended to the dolls two or three times that day, and was sitting listening to the noise the healthy children made as they played in the distance. The long summer holidays had just begun and the children were not at school. From all sides Meli could hear the sound of children's voices, as they played in the streets and yards. The sound drew and enticed her, so that she

153

lost interest in her motionless playmates. She sat listening, but did not go to join the others. She knew well enough that their games were not for her. And the other children would not want her with them. She was too frail, and spoiled their fun. So she sat there longing, and it looked as though she had suddenly become aware of all her difficulties and all she had to bear. She felt how airless it was and how bad the smells; and she saw how ugly and sterile it was all around her. She felt, too, that she was ill and weak. That she was not right. As the minutes passed, she looked more and more despondent, and, gradually, her eyes filled with tears.

All at once, she heard a twang from the telephone wires that passed right above her head, then a shrill peep, a violent fluttering of wings and a bird fell to the ground just in front of her. It was a sparrow that had been careless and flown into one of the wires and dropped in Meli's garden. It fluttered hard in an attempt to get into the air again, but it could only move one wing. The other seemed to be damaged, in some way, and because of that the poor bird could not fly away, but just spun round in circles on the ground. For a little while Meli watched, frightened and unable to move, but then she began edging nearer and nearer, stretched out her hands, drew them in again, made another attempt to take hold of the bird, until at last she succeeded in seizing it in a quick grip. The poor sparrow was terrified and stared at Meli with its black eyes, not daring to move. Meli saw that one wing was hanging limp and tried to lift it. The sparrow jerked with the pain of it, shut its eyes and looked as though it was dead. But Meli paid no attention to that: she carefully felt the wing, looking very knowledgeable, and discovered that the wing-bone was broken.

Colour came into Meli's pale cheeks and her eyes began to shine because now she was interested. She moved across to her playroom under the stone, where she had all sorts of bandages and things. Then, holding the sparrow firmly in one hand, with the other she got out two pieces of stick, a piece or two of cloth and bits of string, and with these she put a splint on the sparrow's wing. That done,

154

she wrapped a piece of cloth round the sparrow so that it would have to stay still; then she laid it down among the ill dolls under the stone.

Meli had scarcely dared breathe while she was doing this; and when she had finished, she was still breathless with emotion. After a little, her mother came out to see what she was doing. There had not been a sound, and there had been no little figure moving to and fro about the boulder as there usually was.

As she stepped outside, Meli's mother saw her sitting on a small stone in front of her playroom, stitching a doll's dress. And she was strangely calm, with no trace of the fears and agitation that were her mother's despair. No, she was quiet and pleased, like someone who had found peace of mind.

When her mother came close, Meli told her in hushed tones

about the sparrow and showed her the bird lying under the boulder. Then her mother understood the reason for Meli's new-found serenity: Meli was playing nurse. There was the same expression on her face, as that on the face of a nurse sitting beside a patient's bed. She had the same gentle tranquility.

"Well, now you'll have to take great care of it and see that it gets well," Meli's mother said.

Meli just nodded. Nurses do not speak unnecessarily in case that disturbs their patients. But her nod said quite clearly that, as far as it rested, with her, the patient would be made well.

"May I see him?" Meli's mother asked, peering down under the boulder.

"But I think it would be best not to touch him," Meli said, "but if you badly want..."

"Good gracious no!" said Meli's mother. "I'm not as inquisitive as that. Let him be."

Then Meli's mother went in, but Meli remained motionless at her post all day. Every time her mother came out to look at her, she was sitting there sewing placidly. There was no question of her longing for the other children now. Having someone to take care of and pity was better than any playmate.

A couple of months later it was still summer and just as hot and lovely as the day the sparrow fell into Meli's garden. In fact, on that arid ground it was hotter and stuffier than ever; and all people who had to work there were glum and moody, just waiting for each day to end. And it was very much the same with the children: they were too sluggish to play. They hung about the level crossing in a great flock waiting for a train to come, or jumping to and fro across the rails. They seldom laughed now, but easily fell to quarreling. They shouted at each other for the least thing, and clinched and fought.

While everyone else was bored and indifferent, the little hunchback's life was one of the greatest interest and excitement. She was continually running in to her mother from her little garden, saying:

"I'm having such fun! Won't you come out and see?"

156

There was not a single doll left in the cave under the boulder. Instead there were a number of cages, some made of cardboard, others of sticks or wire. They were arranged in two rows, as neat and regular as the beds in a hospital; and that was as it should be, for the place under the boulder really was a hospital now. It was full of patients.

Each morning, Meli took out the cages in turn and saw to their occupants. In the largest one she had a lovely white dove that had wounds on its back and head. The poor bird had been in a hawk's talons, but had been saved at the last moment and brought to Meli. And the dove certainly knew that Meli wanted to make it better, for it would press close up to her and lay its head against her cheek, whenever Meli took it out of its cage.

In the next cage was a wagtail that had broken a leg and had a splint put on it. It had recovered enough to be continually trying to stand on its bad leg. The worst thing about the wagtail was not to mend its leg, but to get food for it. Fortunately, lately Meli had acquired a lot of friends who helped her get food for her patients.

Beside the wagtail was a little mouse, sitting quite still and holding its bad leg up. The sight of it always made Meli sad, for this was one patient she could not cure. The poor little mouse had had one foot off in a rat trap. The wound would heal, but the little mouse would have to limp along on three legs for the rest of its life.

There were two kittens as well. They were quite tiny and their eyes weren't open and they could not stand. They were not ill, but their mother had deserted them and they had been brought to Meli to look after.

Ever since Meli had mended the sparrow's broken wing, she had been kept busy looking after sick little animals. She had a wonderful gift for this sort of work and performed real miracle cures. And there was no end to the patience and love she was prepared to lavish on her patients. She would gladly have gone without sleep or food for their sake. And it was all the same to her what kind of animal she had to look after: she would just as gladly care for a young fox or a surly owl, as a little chicken. As long as it was ill she would cherish it and love it. She was so neat and light-fingered that she could have put a splint on a spider's leg.

People had never seen anything as amusing as Meli's hospital. The whole neighbourhood took an interest in what she was doing, and even strangers would come walking out to see her and her sick animals. And every visitor had to admire and wonder that she was able to do what she did. Meli, of course, did not look after her animals in order to be praised for doing so, but all the same it was nice, when people said how clever she was and how nice, and that not everybody could do what she did. It did her good to hear that sort of thing.

Meli's mother realized from the beginning that this was the one thing to occupy and interest her child, and to begin with it was she who found new patients for her; but now she had no need to worry about that. The whole neighbourhood did that for her. Anyone who found a wounded or hurt creature brought it to Meli.

Meli no longer wished she could join the other children at their games. Now, many of the children wanted to come and see her. But not all of them were allowed in now. It was considered a great favour to be admitted inside Meli's fence and allowed to watch her attending to her patients. Big, wild boys would stand still beside her, their only fear that she might not let them stay. They spent most of their spare time getting food for her animals, and doing errands for her. That was the surest way of gaining admittance to her hospital.

But it was not only the big boys that Meli had for her friends; she had all sorts of new ones. There was an old man in the fine grocer's shop in the main street who had a canary which was a wonderful singer and the man loved it more than anything else in the world. Then, one day, the man had tears in his eyes as he served his customers and he told them that his bird was ill, and he was afraid she was going to die. Meli's mother happened to come in that day and heard this and told him that she felt sure her Meli would be able to make the bird better. The man did not answer, but just looked as though she had said something very silly. But the next day he paid a visit to the cottage outside the town and watched Meli tending her patients, and that must have given him confidence in her ability, for a while later he came back with his beloved canary and gave it to her to look after. It almost seemed as though these little creatures were able to tell Meli what was wrong with them; at all events she discovered at once what was the matter with the canary and made it quite well again, and ever after that Meli's mother could never go into that shop without being given a packet of raisins or some sugar-candy to take home to Meli. And the man told all his customers about her, so that Meli became really famous just because of that canary.

Then there was that big dog that before had never wanted to have

anything to do with Meli. It was a dog of habit, who did the same things every day: every morning he went for a walk, which took him past Meli's house, but he always pretended not to see Meli, if she was standing at the gate and called him. But one morning the dog had been limping badly as he went past, and on his way back he had stopped at the gate and lain down and whimpered, as if he could go no further. Meli had gone out to him and looked at his bad paw and very, very carefully pulled out a piece of glass that had gone in between his pads. The next morning, when the dog came past, he was quite all right again; but now he stopped at the gate and waited till Meli came out, then he gave her a paw most beautifully

and licked her hand, before walking on again. And this he did every morning after that, for he was a dog of habit. And it gave Meli great satisfaction to have been able to win over the dog.

It was Meli's father who made all the cages in which she kept her patients. He had never been so nice and loving to Meli before as he was now. Before, he had not wanted to play with her, and had not known what to talk to her about. But ever since Meli had begun looking after her sick animals, he, like others, had become most interested. Now he enjoyed being with her, and had no sooner come home than he would go to see her and ask how the wagtail was or the kittens. And when he came home to lunch, he scarcely allowed himself time to eat. He much preferred being out with Meli and watching her attend to her patients. And he made her all the cages she needed. He was just as keen for Meli's patients to get well as she was; and nothing made Meli happier than being able to share this with him. It put new life into her and she became gay and secure and carefree, like any ordinary child.

It was a sunny summer's day and Meli was sitting on the ground in front of her cave, so preoccupied with what she was doing, that she did not even notice that two nurses in uniform were walking across the open space, heading for her cottage. She never even heard them open the gate and come inside. She never noticed them till they were right close beside her.

Then Meli blushed in surprise, for who had come to see her but her great friend, Sister from the hospital, and Nurse Anna, her next greatest friend. Meli thought that perhaps they had come to see her hospital, but then she thought that was too much to expect. Yet the next moment the sister said:

"Now, Meli, can you show us your hospital? We've been told that you have lots of patients."

Meli blushed and did not want to do so. She felt ashamed of showing her poor little affair to real nurses.

"You've seen our hospital so often, Meli, that you really ought to let us see yours," said the Sister.

165

And so naturally Meli showed them her hospital, and they were both tremendously interested. They asked what was wrong with each of the patients and how Meli was treating them; and Meli was delighted to be able to talk about it with people who really understood.

Meli's mother came out and joined in the conversation, telling them the things Meli had not liked to tell herself, how the big boys had become such friends of hers, and about the big dog and the canary.

As the nurses were leaving, Meli's mother went with them part of the way, so as to be able to talk about Meli.

"She'll make a better nurse than either of us, when she grows up," said the Sister.

"When she grows up," repeated Meli's mother falteringly. "You know what the doctor has said. She cannot live."

"She can now though," Sister replied. "She has begun to grow. And you can see that she now has got something to live for."

And meanwhile Meli stood there in her garden thinking what a wonderful thing it was that Sister and Nurse Anna had been to see her hospital. It was the nicest thing that could have happened. Oh, how happy she was! There was not a child in the whole world as happy as she!

THE LITTLE PRISONER

From the book "The Adventures of Sajo and her Beaver People"

By GREY OWL

The beavers, Chilawee and Chikanee, Big Small and Little Small, were found as deserted babies and brought up to the little American Indian girl, Sajo, to rear. Their devotion to each other and to Sajo is complete and their life very happy until the heartbreaking day when her father announces that the new white trader will not allow their debt to continue until he returns from his winter hunting with the skins to pay it off. The only settlement the trader will accept is one of the tame beavers, for live beavers are valuable. So Chikanee goes away to a zoo in the city. Chilawee pines and Sajo is inconsolable until she persuades her brother, Shapian, to go with her to search for Chikanee in the city. Neither of them has ever been so far, nor do they know the way, but they set out with Chilawee and, after great adventures, they reach the zoo-keeper's office. But Chikanee doesn't know this.

The keeper carried Chikanee to his cottage, which was close by, inside the Park. He had three young children, and when they saw their father bringing in a little beaver, they crowded round to see, and they shouted and clapped their hands with glee, so that Chikanee was afraid again, and tried to burrow into the man's coat; for already he had begun to trust him.

Their father quieted the young ones and set the little creature on the floor, where, finding himself once more in a house, he seemed to feel at home. They all stood watching to see what he would do, and the keeper's wife said: "The wee mite! Look how thin he is, Joey," to one of the youngsters, "go get an apple; those other beavers we used to have were just crazy for apples."

So Joey went and got an apple and put it down on the floor in front of Chikanee. He had never seen an apple before, but he sniffed at it, then, seizing hold of it with both hands, cut into it as best he could with his poor wee broken teeth. Obviously, he found it delicious and demolished nearly half of it. At this the keeper was very pleased, for some of his prisoners refused all food, and died. Now he knew

167

that this poor, battered little animal would recover; somehow he had been none too sure about it. The delighted children laughed to see him sitting up like a little man while he ate, and the keeper's wife exclaimed: "There! Didn't I tell you? He'll be all right in no time."

Then the man brought in the sprays of fresh, juicy poplar leaves he had placed in the pen for Chikanee which before he would not touch, but now he ate eagerly. The children laughed to see him holding the leaves in little bunches in his hands as he crammed them into his mouth. Feeling a good deal better by now, the little creature made small sounds of pleasure while he ate. This overjoyed the young ones, and one – a little girl with golden hair and a round, rosy face – said: "Listen, listen to him talk, just like a little, wee baby! Oh, Daddy, *do* let's keep him in our kitchen!" And their mother spoke up too: "Yes, Alec, let's keep him here for a spell; *don't* take him back – there's no one in the Park. It would be almost like putting a child in prison." And Alec answered: "Perhaps you're right. We'll fix him a place in here for tonight."

So they made a place for Chikanee in the kitchen, and Alec the keeper fastened a low, wide pan of water to the floor, and set a large box down on its side, with plenty of clean straw in it for a bed for him. And there the little beaver spent the night – not entirely happily perhaps, but very comfortably.

The next morning Alec returned him to his cage, so that any of

the public who came to the Park could see him; but when evening came round again and the grounds were empty, the keeper brought him back to the cottage. And from then on he did this every day, and Chikanee spent all the hours when he was not "working" in the keeper's house, and in the kitchen had his bed, and his big pan of water, and ate his leaves and twigs there. And each day he had a nice, juicy apple, which quite made up for a lot of his troubles, though not for all of them; for never in his prisoner's life would he be anything but lonesome, so long as he lived.

Every morning there was a considerable mess of peeled sticks, and cut branches, and left-over leaves to clean, and the floor was all slopped up with water, but the children willingly turned to and cleaned up, after he was carried away to his daily task of being stared at in the cage. Nobody seemed to mind the little trouble he was. He got along famously with the family and, in his own small way, soon became quite a part of the household.

As time went on Chikanee got to know them all, and he would romp clumsily with the youngsters; and to them he was a kind of tumbling, good-natured toy, a good deal like one of those roguish wool puppies to be found on Christmas trees. But to Chikanee, it could never be the same as it had been at his first home – the forest O-pee-pee-soway; and often he didn't want to play, but lay quietly in his box, his little heart filled with a great empty longing for his old playmates.

Before very long his teeth had grown in, and he spent a lot of time sharpening them against one another, grinding and rattling them together at a great rate. He now gave his coat – which he had sadly neglected for a time, so that it had become all tangled and awry –

its daily scrubbing and combing, and his small frame, that had for a while been little more than a bag of bones, soon filled out, and he began to look like the old Chikanee again. And in a way he was happy; but never quite.

Daytimes, in the cage, he was really miserable. The keeper knew this, and always felt badly when he put the little fellow in there each morning, and looked back at this pitiful little creature that gazed after him so wistfully as he walked away, sitting there alone on the bare cement floor, surrounded by bars that would have held a grizzly bear. The keeper knew that a beaver can live twenty or more years – twenty years in a prison of iron and concrete! In twenty years the keeper's own family would be grown up and away from there; indeed, he himself might be gone! The town would have become a great city (it was not really a very big place); people would come and go – free people, happy people – and through it all, this unhappy little beast, who had done no harm to anyone, and seemed only to want someone to be kind to him, would, for twenty long and lonely years, look out through the bars of that wretched pen as though he had been some violent criminal; waiting for the freedom that would never be his; waiting only to die at last. And, thought the keeper, for no good reason at all, except that a few thoughtless people, who never really cared if they ever saw a beaver, could stare for a minute or two at the unhappy little prisoner – then go away and forget they had ever seen him. Somehow, this kind-hearted man thought, it did not seem fair, and when he watched the little creature rollicking with the children in his funny, clumsy way, he wished very much that there was something that he could do about it. He decided to make his small prisoner as happy as he could, and to continue to give him the freedom of the cottage as long as it was at all possible.

But Chikanee had not quite given up; he had one hope that for a long time he never lost. He quite expected that, in some mysterious way, his dear friend Chilawee would come to join him; for in the old days, no matter where he had happened to be, it had not been

171

long before Chilawee had turned up, looking for him. And so, every so often, he searched for him very carefully, looking in the wooden hut that stood in a corner of his cage. At the cottage he searched patiently all through the downstairs rooms and would sometimes take a run outside and examine the woodshed very thoroughly – very sure that some day he would again find him. But after a whole month of daily disappointments he began to lose his courage, and at last gave up his search that always turned out to be such a failure.

Hundreds of miles away, Chilawee was doing the very same thing – and all for nothing.

Chikanee was just commencing to forget about searching, when something took place that was the very worst of all – and yet something that was very near to his dearest wish. One day an Indian woman, with a bright shawl on her head, passed by the pen. The moment he saw her, Chikanee dashed wildly to the bars and reached through them with clutching paws. He let out a piercing cry, for fear she would pass him by. Hearing this, the woman stopped and spoke to him, and the sounds she made were the same as he had heard so often in the Indian country, at home! But not the voice. And seeing her face, and catching the scent of her, he turned and plodded slowly back to the bare wooden hut again, more dejected and downcast than he had ever been.

He had thought it was Sajo.

But this experience stirred him, and brought new hopes to him; he got the idea that some day Sajo *would* come. And from then on he watched for her. Crowds of people visited the Park in the afternoons, and most of them paused by his cage to see what a beaver was like. But his "customers" never stayed long, and soon passed on; to most of them he looked to be just a scrubby little pup with a flat tail. Some just gazed carelessly, others curiously; a few poked sticks at him and made harsh and, as he thought, threatening sounds; a few – a very few – pitied him, and one or two were friendly and gave him peanuts and candy.

172

But none of them was Sajo. Chikanee continued to hope, however, and spent his time watching closely every face he saw, sniffing every hand he could get near to. But he never saw the face looked for, never caught the scent of that so-loved little hand. Yet he was sure that some day a well-remembered voice would call out "Chik-a-nee!", that the small brown hands whose touch had so often thrilled his little body, would again pick him up, and then – oh! The joy of once more pushing his nose close into that special spot in a certain warm, soft neck, there to puff and blow a little while and then to go to sleep there, and forget!

Hours at a time he spent this way, watching, waiting, hoping; and later, on his little pallet in the cottage kitchen, he would think, in some dim and misty way, of the happy days that seemed now to have been oh, so long ago, and thought of the little chamber under Shapian's bed that Chilawee and he had between them for their very own; and of the crazy, tiny beaver house, and all the other arrangements at which they had worked so bravely together.

As time passed, at last he became listless, and kept to himself, even when he was supposed to be happy in the kitchen. He never played with the children any more. He neglected his coat, so that it became matted and unkempt. He began to refuse his food, and would sit with his apple untouched in his hands, his little head drooping, eyes closed, breathing fast and heavily.

And the keeper, looking at him sorrowfully, knew that there was no longer any need to worry about the twenty years; or any years. Chikanee wasn't going to live.

Now the wee brain grew hot and feverish with longing, and he seemed sometimes almost to see and hear his old play-fellows there

before him, and, thinking of them, fell asleep, and sleeping, surely must have dreamed of them.

One evening Chikanee awoke from what must have been a dream so real that he thought himself once more at home with his loved ones, and he started up and ran whimpering about the kitchen, looking for them and, not finding them, cried out again and again in loud sobbing wails, from very lonesomeness and misery. And as he cried, his voice was like the voice of a small, lost child.

What he did not, *could* not know, was that less than one mile away, in another and similar room, was another and similar little beaver, and that there with him, waiting for morning, too excited to even think of sleeping, were two little Indians – a boy who stood straight and proudly, like an arrow, and a little girl wearing a brightly-coloured head-shawl. And in one corner of the room there stood an old familiar well-worn, birch-bark basket.

Yes, it is true – it was Sajo and Shapian. They had come, at last.

It is doubtful if either Sajo or Shapian remembered very much about that trip to the amusement park, up to the time that Pat pointed out the entrance that could now be seen, not far ahead of them. Then Sajo started to run. She was not pale now, and her eyes, that had been so dry and staring, were all aglow. Her shawl fell back unheeded, and her braids flew out and bobbed up and down on her shoulders as her little moccasined feet pattered on the pavement. Behind her came Shapian, unable to keep up with her on account of carrying the basket, inside which Chilawee, tired of being cooped up for so long, was making a great uproar. Next came the stalwart Mr. O'Reilly, very red in the face, his helmet off, dabbing with his large red hand-kerchief at the head that had been "bald as an egg for twenty years", puffing and blowing like a tug-boat that had a light touch of asthma.

Once he bellowed, "Hey! What *is* this – a race?" But the young-sters kept going right on, and it is very doubtful if they even heard him; so he fell to grumbling, "the little haythens, they'll be the death of me yet, so they will". But he kept valiantly on.

Several passers-by stopped to look at the young Indians in their

forest clothes, racing along the street with the policeman apparently chasing them. They heard, too, the shrill cries and wails coming out of the basket, as Chilawee objected loudly to the shaking up he was getting in all this hurry; so a few of them turned and joined this strange parade, and followed this small, running, black-haired girl.

There was some delay at the entrance, as the Park was not yet open for the day, but O'Reilly soon caught up, and showed his card of credentials, and they were let in. Quite a respectable crowd had gathered following them, and they pushed in with them as soon as the gates were opened. The attendant, who was Alec, the keeper, already knew what to do, as Mr. H—— had decided, at the last moment, to come too, and had given orders and now stood in the crowd. At a nod from Mr. H——, the keeper led Sajo quickly over towards the beaver pen. And all at once the little girl was as pale as a ghost again. She seemed to be running in a great empty space at the end of which, miles away, was a dark, ugly-looking row of iron bars, and now, now – she could see through them, and there – yes, there was a brown, furry little animal sitting up in the centre of them, and – oh! was it? – could it be? – yes, it *was*, Chikanee!!

And Sajo, no longer shy, forgot the watching people, forgot the noisy city, forgot everything but the small furry body that was now so close. Rushing to the iron fence, she threw herself on her knees in the gravel, thrust her two arms through the bars, and screamed "Chikanee! CHIKANEE!! CHIKANEE!!!"

The little beaver, not believing, sat without a move, just looking.

"It's *me* – Sajo! Oh, Chikanee!" The cry was almost a wail. (Oh, had he *forgotten*?)

For a moment longer the little creature stood there, stock still, his chubby brown head cocked to one side, listening, as Sajo cried out again: *"Chik-a-nee-e-e ! ! !"* – and then *he knew!* And with a funny little noise in his throat, he scrambled as fast as his short legs would carry him to the bars.

At that a little cheer broke out amongst the crowd, and there was a small commotion. And Alec the keeper now came forward and opened a small iron gate, and said, "This way, Miss – a – Mam'selle – a – Senorita –" for he didn't quite know how he should address a little Indian girl, and was rather excited himself. Sajo rushed in, knelt down, gathered the so-long-lost Chikanee up on her lap and bent over him; and they were both very still. And the gay head-shawl hid everything; and neither you, nor I, nor anyone else will ever know just what passed between those two on that fateful, that glorious, that never-to-be-forgotten morning. The grey-haired Mr. H—— took his handkerchief from his pocket and blew his nose rather loudly; and Alec the keeper had suddenly become troubled with a cough. "Humph," he said, "hurrumph."

"You bet," exclaimed Pat the policeman in a hearty voice, although the keeper hadn't really said anything at all.

176

And now was to come the biggest thrill of all. Chilawee and Chikanee were to have *their* party now: they were only ten feet apart, and didn't know it! What a thrill was ahead! So it was with wildly beating heart that Sajo and Shapian carried the basket in, pulled off the lid, lifted Chilawee out and set him down a few feet away from Chikanee. Then they stood and watched, breathlessly.

For a second or two neither of the beavers moved – they just stared at each other. Then, the truth slowly dawning in the little twilight minds, they crept towards one another, eyes almost starting out of their heads, ears wide open, listening, sniffing, creeping slowly forward until the creep became a walk, the walk became a little shuffling trot – then, sure at last, the trot broke suddenly into a gallop, and with a rush they met, head-on. So violent was the collision, that they went straight up on end, and with loud shrill cries they grasped each other tightly, and there, in front of all those people, began to wrestle!

The ceaseless, hopeless searching, the daily disappointments, all the misery and longing, the dreary empty nights of lonesomeness – were over!

Big Small and Little Small were together again.

PLATERO AND I

From the book of the same title

By JUAN RAMON JIMÉNEZ

Loving his little silvery donkey, Platero, his constant companion and
extension of himself, who carries the old man all around the Spanish village
of Moguer where they both live, Juan Ramón Jiménez writes down bits
of their experience together. Some of what he writes (in his beautiful
book, *Platero and I*) is directed to the little donkey. Some of it is about
Platero, his name as silver as his coat. Of this book by the winner of the
1956 Nobel Prize for literature the French journal, *Figaro*, has said, "If
there are in world literature two or three books capable of giving to people
their childhood soul, *Platero and I* is among them."

When I go to see Platero at noon, a transparent ray of the midday
sun is kindling a great patch of gold on the soft silver of his back.
Beneath his body, on the dark ground, which is vaguely green and
tinges everything with emerald, the old roof rains clear coins of
fire.

Diana, who has been playing between Platero's legs, comes dancing toward me and puts her forepaws on my chest, eager to lick
my mouth with her pink tongue. Perched on the highest part of the
manger, the goat regards me with curiosity, moving her delicate
head from side to side with feminine distinction. In the meantime,
Platero, who had already greeted me with uplifted voice before I
entered, tries to break free from his rope, bringing all his gay
sturdiness into play.

The skylight lets in the iridescent treasure of the Zenith, and
through it I climb for a moment up a sunbeam to the sky, away
from these friends. Presently, back on earth, I step on a rock and
look out upon the fields. The green landscape is swimming in the
fragrant and drowsy flood of noonlight, and against the clear blue
framed by the grimy walls breaks the sweet ringing of a bell.

We understand each other. I let him go at his fancy, and he always
takes me where I want to go. Platero knows that on reaching the

Corona pine I like to get close to its trunk and touch it, and to look up at the sky through its enormous, light-filtered top; he knows that the narrow path that leads between grassplots to the Old Fountain delights me; that it is high festival for me to watch the river from the pine hill, which, like a sorceress, brings classic scenes before me. If I go to sleep, unafraid, on his back, my awakening always finds me at one of these friendly spots.

I treat Platero as if he were a child. If the road is rough or a little too hard for him, I get down to make it easy for him. I kiss him; I tease him mercilessly. He knows that I love him, and bears me no grudge. He is so like me – so different from the rest – that I have come to believe that he dreams my own dreams.

If you would come to kindergarten with the other children, Platero, you would learn the ABC's and you would learn to write. You would know more than the donkey in the wax figures, the little mermaid's friend who appears garlanded with artificial flowers through the crystal which shows the mermaid all rosy flesh and gold in her green element. You would know more than the doctor and than the village priest, Platero.

But, although you are only four, you are so big and clumsy. In what little chair could you sit, at what table could you write, what paper and what pen would do for you, where in the chorus could you sing, say, the Credo?

No, Platero, no. You come with me. I will show you the flowers and the stars. And no one shall laugh at you as at a stupid child, nor shall anyone place on your head, as if you were what they call an ass, the ridiculous dunce cap with ears twice as long as yours.

On entering the pasture lands Platero begins limping. I jump quickly to the ground. "What is the matter, child?"

Platero lets his right forefoot hang limp without weight or strength, barely touching the burning sand of the road, showing the frog of the hoof.

With greater solicitude, no doubt, than that shown him by old

183

Darbon, his doctor, I stoop to examine the bruised foot. A long green orange-tree thorn is stuck in it like a little round emerald dagger. All sympathy with Platero's pain, I pull the thorn and take the poor fellow to the brook of the yellow lilies so that the running water may lave the little wound with its long pure tongue.

Then we go on toward the white sea, I leading, he following, still limping, his head knocking softly against my body at each faltering step.

One day the green canary – I do not know how or why – flew out of his cage. He was an old bird – a sad legacy from a dead woman – which I had not set at liberty for fear that he might starve or freeze to death, or that he might be eaten by the cats.

All morning long he flew about the pomegranate blossoms in the garden, through the pine tree by the gate, among the lilacs. And all morning long the children sat on the porch, absorbed in the brief flights of the yellowish bird. Platero rested close to the rose-bushes, playing with a butterfly.

In the late afternoon the canary came to the roof of the large house, and there he remained a long time, fluttering in the soft light of the setting sun. Of a sudden, without anyone's knowing how or why, he appeared in his cage, gay once more.

What a stir in the garden! The children leaped about, clapping their hands, rosy and laughing as the dawn; Diana, mad with joy, followed them, barking at her own tinkling bell; having caught their mirth, Platero capered around like wild young goat, stood on his hind legs dancing a rude waltz, and then, standing on his fore-feet, kicked his hind feet in the clear warm air . . .

In the big creek, which the rains had swelled as far as the vineyard, we found an old cart stuck in the mud, lost to view under its load of grass and oranges. A ragged, dirty little girl was weeping over one wheel, trying to help the donkey, who was, alas, smaller and frailer than Platero. And the little donkey was spending himself against the wind trying vainly at the sobbing cry of the child to pull the cart out of the mire. His efforts were futile, like the efforts of brave children, like the breath of those tired summer breezes which fall fainting among the flowers.

I patted Platero, and as well as I could I hitched him to the cart in front of the wretched little donkey. I encouraged him then with an affectionate command, and Platero, at one tug, pulled cart and beast out of the mud and up the bank.

How the little girl smiled! It was as if the evening sun, setting among the yellow-crystal rain clouds, had kindled a dawn of joy behind her dirty tears.

With tearful gladness she offered me two choice oranges, perfect, heavy, round. I took them gratefully, and I gave one to the weak little donkey, to comfort him; the other to Platero, as a golden reward.

Since we have come to the capital, I have wanted Platero to see the orchard. We walk very slowly along the iron grille in the grateful shade of the acacias and banana trees, which are still loaded with fruit. Platero's footsteps resound on the pavement, which is moistly bright from its watering, blue with the reflected sky in places, and in places white with wet fallen flowers exhaling a sweet evanescent delicate aroma.

Through the open spaces of the dripping ivy on the iron grille, what coolness and what an odor rise from the drenched garden. Within, children play. And through that wave of whiteness the little carriage with its little purple flags and green awning goes by shrilly tinkling! The hazelnut-vendor's boat passes, all adorned in garnet and gold with its long strings of peanuts and its smoking chimney stack; the balloon girl with her gigantic floating bouquet

of blue and green and red; the taffy-seller, exhausted under his red box ... In the sky, through the mass of verdure already tinged by the sickness of autumn, against which the cypress and the palm stand out, the yellowish moon begins to glow between rosy clouds.

At the gateway when I am about to enter, the blue man who guards it with his yellow stick and his great silver watch, says to me:

"The donkey may not enter, sir."

"The donkey? *What* donkey?" I say, looking beyond Platero, having forgotten, naturally, his animal form.

"What donkey could I mean, sir, what donkey could I mean?"

Then, realizing the truth, since Platero "may not enter", being a donkey, I, being a man, refuse to; and I go with him along the grille, patting him and talking with him of other things ... of many beautiful things.

FOXY

From the book of the same title

By JOHN MONTGOMERY

Quiet and subdued, the young orphan boy David, adopted by Mr. and
Mrs. Hedger, has been slow at fitting into the life on their small chicken
farm. He has few school friends. The one great secret joy of his days is
a little fox, hidden in the barn. He had found the pretty cub in the woods a
few weeks earlier and tended it unobserved. Now the O'Briens who live
nearby have lost some chickens and believe a fox is responsible.

The boy ran nearly all the way home, passing the O'Briens' bungalow
faster than ever before. There were still some feathers in the lane.
But when he went into the kitchen to announce his return, Mrs.
Hedger immediately asked him to help lay the table for tea, so it
was later than usual when he crept into the barn and opened the door
of the inner room. The bundle of meat bulged in his pocket, and here
was Foxy jumping up to greet him, but the leather lead was no
longer attached to the collar; the cub had broken free. And under the
wooden wall of the old barn was a gaping hole and freshly turned
earth, showing all too clearly what had happened in the night.

David did not pause to consider that it was strange that Foxy had returned. He only knew that it must be his fox which had killed the chickens and made himself the enemy of everyone in the district. The thought frightened him. What if it happened again, perhaps with their own hens, and Foxy was shot?

Not that the cub looked at all guilty. He just put his nose well down into the piece of newspaper and gobbled up his meal. Then after he had chased the paper around in the straw, he looked up at his young master, yawned, and sat back and began to lick his front paws. But there was a small piece of bracken leaf still clinging to

his brush, and as David removed it he wondered where it had come from. Most of the bracken was up in the wood. Had Foxy been there? If so, he had probably not been to the O'Briens'.

But who could tell what had occurred in the night?

"Have you been after the chickens?" he asked, but the cub only yawned again. "If you go out again they'll shoot you – they'll *kill* you." And the mere thought brought a lump into his throat.

The clasp of the lead was broken off at the collar, so he had to double it through and twist it back. And now came the time when the cub would, in ordinary circumstances, be taken for his evening walk, secretly and stealthily. But this was no ordinary day, and what happened next was unexpected and frightening.

Crossing the yard or slipping unseen around the side of the barn was always the most difficult part of the walk, there was the chance that someone would be watching from the house. He had to pick the cub up and tuck him half under his jacket, edging along the wooden wall of the barn until he came to the gap that divided it from the beginning of the thorn hedge. Then he usually made a dash for cover, hoping that if anyone saw him they would think he was running out to play. But this was an unlucky day, nothing went right. No sooner had he started to run across the gap, hugging the cub close against his chest, than he heard a voice from the house call, "David!"

He stopped, as if frozen solid. And in that awful second, between running and stopping, his foot caught on a loose stone and down he went headlong on the gravel, his right arm outstretched to take his weight, his left still clutching the precious bundle.

He tried, even as he realized what had happened, to lie still so that Foxy couldn't be seen, but it was no use. The fox, surprised by the fall, had already twisted himself free and was standing on the ground, vigorously shaking himself and making little whining noises. The game was up, they were discovered.

"David!" called Mr. Hedger from the doorway. He sounded surprised, and now, with long strides, he came towards them.

"Are you all right?"

"Yes," murmured David, biting his lower lip and wondering what would happen.

"What on earth is *this?*" Mr. Hedger sounded severe. "Where did you get it from?" His dark eyebrows stood out bushier than ever.

"It's mine," said the boy. "He's quite harmless – he's tame – he wouldn't hurt anything, really he wouldn't – he isn't a *wild* fox – look – he's on a lead."

"But where did you get him?"

"I've had him for *ages*. He's quite tame, really he is." And just at that moment, the cub, excited by the urgency of his master's appeal, licked him on the nose.

"See!" said David, picking himself up, "he's much better than a dog." He began to brush down his clothes with his hands.

Mr. Hedger came near and looked at Foxy.

"But where have you kept him?" he asked.

"In the barn – tied up – he's quite safe there, at the back, in the harness-room. You wouldn't even know he was there at all."

"I didn't," said Mr. Hedger. "And what about food?"

It took only a few minutes for the boy to explain how he had looked after the fox. When it was all over, Mr. Hedger put his hand down and felt Foxy's back. "Seems strong enough," he said, "but you know, it won't do."

"Why not? I can keep him, can't I? You're not going to take him away?"

"But David boy, you can't have a fox on a chicken farm. He'll kill them. Perhaps he's the one that took Bill O'Brien's hens last night. It wouldn't be fair to keep him in a poultry district."

David said: "But he's never even *touched* a chicken. He'll *never* eat chickens if he's given real dinner, and he has *tons* of meat. Foxes never kill chickens if they have proper dinners."

"I'm sorry," said Mr. Hedger, "but a fox is quite impossible on a farm. He'll have to go. If we don't get rid of him, one of the other farmers is sure to shoot him, sooner or later, anyhow."

193

"But they *couldn't*, they can't shoot my fox, he's *mine*! I *found* him, no one is allowed to shoot him!" There were tears in David's eyes which threatened to run down his face, which had to be held back with a sniff. But perhaps Mr. Hedger sensed they were there, because when he spoke again he sounded a little kinder, as if – after all – the situation wasn't so hopeless.

"Well, I don't know," he said, "I just don't know. You'd better bring it into the house, and we'll see what can be done."

So instead of going for their walk they followed him into the farmhouse and there, around the kitchen table, Mr. and Mrs. Hedger and David discussed the future of the cub, which lay curled up on the fibre mat by the boy's feet.

Mrs. Hedger had taken to it at once. She declared it was one of the most attractive animals she'd ever seen. David was very grateful for that, and surprised that she showed no fear when she patted Foxy on his back, and stroked his head. In a way, it was probably because she made a fuss of the little fellow that Mr. Hedger changed his mind. But it took a good half hour of discussion and argument before he agreed that Foxy should have his chance. If he behaved himself, he could stay; but if he killed anything or went out hunting – he would have to go.

It was such an important moment, when Mr. Hedger made his decision, that David could hardly believe it; he jumped down from his chair and ran around to where he sat, and hugged him. He had never done it before; it seemed now that Mr. Hedger, with his fierce bushy eyebrows, was almost like his real father.

Mr. Hedger took out a red pocket handkerchief and blew his nose, hard. Then he said: "Well, we might as well start at once. We'd better take him into the chicken run and introduce him to some of the hens."

"But if he *goes* for them?" said Mrs. Hedger.

David said, "Oh, he'll never do *that* – you'll see."

"We'll show him the birds," said Mr. Hedger, "and restrain him, so he will learn not to attack them. It isn't as if he were a vixen with seven cubs to feed."

The vixen, thought David – wondering if it was she who had crept down from the wood and taken Mr. O'Brien's chickens.

"The trouble is," said Mr. Hedger, "that you can never be quite sure with animals unless you train them very carefully. You can have wild dogs and wild cats, all much more savage than the tame ones. But we'll give the cub a fair chance to learn."

"Oh, thank you," said David.

Mr. Hedger said, "But you'll have to be careful of the hunt."

"Surely they wouldn't hurt a *tame* fox?" asked the boy. "Why do they hunt, anyway?"

Mr. Hedger said, "You'll never quite understand why people hunt, until you join in. Hunting is a matter of emotion, mostly primitive, going back to the times before people thought kindly about animals or reasoned properly."

"But it isn't *right*, is it?" asked David. It was difficult to reconcile the fact that men and women on horses rode out with hounds – specially trained to kill – across the countryside to catch the kind of creature that Foxy would become. Didn't they have dogs and cats of their own at home? And here was the cub curled up in front of the fire, asleep. Hunting didn't make sense.

"Most of them do it because they like riding," explained Mr. Hedger. "Very few people are naturally cruel – they are just thoughtless. You see, the fox is traditionally the enemy of man, even though he kills rats and mice and rabbits. I know it isn't logical – any more than bullfighting is, but you have to remember that these old traditional sports are relics of medieval times, and they die hard. Many years ago people used to watch bear-baiting, and cock-fighting, and other unpleasant pastimes – and they called them sports, just as fox hunting and deer-hunting and going after otters, and coursing hares – they're all known as sports, although in many countries they are forbidden. But even in fox-hunting the fox stands a chance. Only about one in ten is actually killed by the hunt."

195

"What happens to the others?"

"They're shot by farmers, or they get caught in traps."

"Traps?"

"Rabbit traps, or mole traps, steel springs with teeth. An animal can lose a paw or pad in one of those things, or worse still the trap gets fixed to the paw and stays there – dragged along – until the creature dies, unable to find food because the other animals hear him coming. So you see, you've got to look after Foxy very well. It's quite a responsibility, even more than having a dog.

"I'm sure he'll be all right," said Mrs. Hedger.

"Oh, he will, he will," said David earnestly.

By mid-August, when the wheat fields were deepest golden brown and the wind rustled through the ripening ears, the cub was almost fully grown. It was surprising, the way everyone accepted him – Mr. O'Brien, when shown him on the end of the lead, was sure Foxy was much smaller than the one he had seen in the moonlight, dragging away a chicken. In fact, the O'Briens liked the cub very much, and were inclined to give him chocolate biscuits.

Even more strange was the way the village dogs accepted him. It was as if they knew he was one of their own kind; they just sniffed at him and left him alone.

Soon not only the cub, but also his young master was called "Foxy."

"Hullo, Foxy!" Charlie said one day at the school gate, and the name had stuck, spreading around the village. David rather liked it. People who had never talked to David or noticed him now stopped to chat, and were smiling and pleasant. Everyone knew the little boy with the fox.

There was now no need for secrecy, and the days need not be spent in the harness-room. Foxy still slept there at night, but during school time he was allowed in the kitchen, where he stayed curled up in a large wooden box which Mr. Hedger had made for him, lying on warm blankets close to the fire. At four-thirty, when his young master returned from school, he was ready to be taken out.

And because everyone in Woodmere knew about him and accepted him, he could now go further afield, there was almost no limit provided he was within sight and under control. The way the young fox scampered about on the soft turf, tumbling over in the sunshine, was a delight to see, and suddenly David was wonderfully happy. He was at peace with the world – and he had his very special friend, Foxy . . . and his family.

199

KOKA THE COCKATOO

From the book "King Solomon's Ring"

By KONRAD Z. LORENZ

> Dr. Lorenz is a remarkable Austrian naturalist whose universally popular
> books, which sell all over the world, not only give great pleasure to the
> reader but also make a genuine contribution to scientific knowledge. This
> is especially true of his studies of birds with whom he communicates to
> a unique degree. This sometimes leads to onlookers thinking him mad as
> he fears in the first episode of this story.

The third time that I was in danger of being delivered up to the
psychiatric clinic was the fault of my big yellow-crested cockatoo
Koka. I had bought this beautiful and very tame bird shortly before
Easter, for a considerable sum of money. It was many weeks before the poor fellow had overcome the mental disturbances caused
by his long imprisonment. At first he could not realize that he was
no longer fettered and could now move about freely. It was a pitiable
sight to see this proud creature sitting on a branch, ever and anon
preparing himself for flight, but not daring to take off, because he
could not believe that he was no longer on the chain. When at last
he had overcome this inward resistance he became a lively and
exuberant being and developed a strong attachment for my person.
As soon as he was let out of the room in which we still shut him
up at night-time, he flew straight off to find me, displaying thereby an
astonishing intelligence. In quite a short time he realized where I was
probably to be found. At first he flew to my bedroom window, and,
if I was not there, down to the duck pond; in short, he visited all the
sites of my morning inspection at the various animal pens in our
research station. This determined quest was not without danger to
the cockatoo because, if he failed to find me, he extended his search
farther and farther and had several times lost his way on such occasions. Accordingly, my fellow workers had strict instructions not
to let the bird out during my absence.

One Saturday in June, I got off the train from Vienna at Altenberg station, in the midst of a gathering of bathers, such as often flock to our village at fine weekends. I had gone only a few steps along the street and the crowd had not yet dispersed when, high above me in the air, I saw a bird whose species I could not at first determine. It flew with slow, measured wing-beats, varied at set intervals by longer periods of gliding. It seemed too heavy to be a buzzard; for a stork it was not big enough and, even at that height, neck and feet should have been visible. Then the bird gave a sudden swerve so that the setting sun shone for a second full on the underside of the great wings which lit up like stars in the blue of the skies. The bird was white. By Heaven, it was my cockatoo! The steady movements of his wings clearly indicated that he was setting out on a long-distance flight. What should I do? Should I call to the bird? Well, have you ever heard the flight-call of the greater yellow-crested cockatoo? No? But you have probably heard pig-killing after the old method. Imagine pig squealing at its most voluminous, taken up by a microphone and magnified many times by a good loudspeaker. A man can imitate it quite successfully, though somewhat feebly, by bellowing at the top of his voice "O-ah!" I had already proved that the cockatoo understood this imitation and promptly "came to heel". But would it work at such a height? A bird always has great difficulty in making the decision to fly downwards at a steep angle. To yell, or not to yell, that was the question. If I yelled and the bird came down, all would be well, but what if it sailed calmly on through the clouds? How would I then explain my song to the crowd of people? Finally, I did yell. The people around me stood still, rooted to the spot. The bird hesitated for a moment on outstretched wings, then, folding them, it descended in one dive and landed upon my outstretched arm. Once again I was master of the situation.

On another occasion, the frolics of this bird gave me quite a serious fright. My father, by that time an old man, used to take his siesta at the foot of a terrace on the south-west side of our house.

For medical reasons, I was never quite happy to think of him exposed to the glaring mid-day sun, but he would let nobody break him of his old habit. One day, at his siesta time, I heard him, from his accustomed place, swearing like a trooper, and as I raced round the corner of the house, I saw the old gentleman swaying up the drive in a cramped position, bending forwards, his arms tightly folded about his waist. "In heaven's name, are you ill?" "No," came the embittered response, "I am not ill, but that confounded creature has bitten all the buttons off my trousers while I was fast asleep!" And that is what had happened. Eye-witnesses at the scene of the crime discovered, laid out in buttons, the whole outline of the old professor: here the arms, there the waistcoat, and here, unmistakably, the buttons off his trousers.

One of the nicest cockatoo-tricks which, in fanciful inventiveness, equalled the experiments of monkey or human children, arose from the ardent love of the bird for my mother who, so long as she stayed in the garden in summertime, knitted without stopping. The cockatoo seemed to understand exactly how the soft skeins worked and what the wool was for. He always seized the free end of the wool with his beak and then flew lustily into the air, unravelling the ball behind him. Like a paper kite with a long tail, he climbed high and then flew in regular circles round the great lime tree which stood in front of our house. Once, when nobody was there to stop him he encircled the tree, right up to its summit, with brightly coloured woollen strands which it was impossible to disentangle from the widespreading foliage. Our visitors used to stand in mute astonishment before this tree, and were unable to understand how and why it had been thus decorated.

The cockatoo paid court to my mother in a very charming way, dancing round her in the most grotesque fashion, folding and unfolding his beautiful crest and following her wherever she went. If she were not there, he sought her just as assiduously as he had been used, in his early days, to search for me. Now my mother had no less than four sisters. One day these aunts, in company with some equally aged ladies of their acquaintance, were partaking of tea on the veranda of our house. They sat at a huge round table, a plate of luscious home-grown strawberries in front of each, and in the middle of the table, a large, very shallow bowl of finest icing sugar. The cockatoo, who was flying accidentally or wittingly past, espied, from without, my mother who was presiding at this festive board. The next moment, with a perilous dive, he steered himself through

the doorway, which, though wide, was nevertheless narrower than the span of his wings. He intended to land before my mother on the table where he was accustomed to sit and keep her company while she knitted; but this time he found the runway encumbered with numerous obstacles to flying technique and, into the bargain, he was in the midst of unknown faces. He considered the situation, pulled himself up abruptly in mid-air, hovering over the table like a helicopter, then, turning on his own axis, he opened the throttle again and the next second had disappeared. So also had the icing sugar from the shallow bowl, out of which the propeller wind had wafted every grain. And around the table sat seven powdered ladies, seven rococo ladies whose faces, like lepers', were white as snow and who held their eyes tight shut. Beautiful!

DINAH WAS A MANTIS

From the book "Near Horizons"

By EDWIN WAY TEALE

Edwin Way Teale cultivates his insect garden in an old apple orchard on
a hillside not far from New York. Here he grows all the plants most
attractive to insects so that he can study the activities of his visitors and
residents undisturbed. Here Dinah made her first appearance.

Any "Who's Who" of my garden insects should give a prominent
place to Dinah. She was the most memorable of all my hillside
acquaintances. She was viewed with interest by scientists. She even
had her brief moment on Broadway. And for a time she seemed
indestructible.

The French philosopher, Blaise Pascal, once remarked of human
beings: "The present is never our end; past and present are means.
The future alone is our end. And so we never live, but always hope
to live, and, always trying to be happy at some future time, it inevitably comes to pass that we never attain the goal."

Dinah lived life on a different plan. She gave no thought for the
morrow – or even for the next instant. Her whole attention was
occupied by that thin ridge of time which lies between the past and
the future. The living prey closest to her spiked forelegs obscured
all other considerations.

I first met Dinah on a dusty September afternoon. South of the
garden, a tangled mass of interlacing weeds and vines rose higher
than my waist. Reared up on the crest of this green mound, a five-
inch insect, also green, sat motionless, its forelegs folded meekly
in an attitude of prayer. As we stood facing each other, there was a
flick of movement, a slight scraping sound, among the vines between
us. A small garter snake was exploring the dense vegetation fully
three feet above the ground. It saw me and became motionless – like
a striped thicker vine in the midst of the tangle. It was headed toward

the spot where the mantis now swayed slowly from side to side. The garter snake was hardly its own length away.

Obeying an impulse as old as the Garden of Eden, I sided against the serpent. With a small twig I tapped it smartly on the tail. It slid rapidly away down out of sight. At the moment, I fancied that I had saved the life of the praying mantis. But later, as I became more familiar with the character and capacities which lay behind that meek exterior I began to suspect that maybe I had saved the life of the snake instead.

When I looked again, the insect was hurrying away over the green, mass, its forelegs alternately reaching far ahead like a man swimming overhand. I made a grab for it and it unfurled four gauzy wings and sailed away. Its neck stretched far in front, mallard-wise, and its cigar-shaped abdomen extending to the rear gave it the appearance of two insects flying in tandem. At the end of a hundred feet, it landed awkwardly on a goldenrod. I picked it off by the scruff of the neck, so to speak, where its grasping spiked forelegs could not reach my fingers. After a moment's struggle, it hung passively between my thumb and forefinger.

Established on a plant in my study at home, Dinah watched me curiously, her great-eyed, pointed head turning this way and that to follow my movements. As the days passed, my ways seemed as mystifying to her as her ways were to me. She would study me intently for minutes at a time with her head cocked on one side like a puppy. The pencil sharpener on my study wall engaged her attention for long periods of time. She would clamber over it, touch it with her antennae, sit for minutes perched on the handle surveying it intently. Her favorite resting place in the room was the top of a picture frame hung above my desk, probably because, I liked to think, the frame held the photograph of the reared praying mantis which formed the frontispiece of *Grassroot Jungles*, an earlier book of mine.

A praying mantis has no voice. But Dinah was far from noiseless. She made rustling sounds in my papers; her feet ticked along the varnished wood of the desk; she produced sudden thumps when she landed. In walking she frequently used a middle leg in an exploratory manner like a daddy-long-legs, setting it down several times before shifting her weight to it. Three taps were the usual number before a final decision was reached. For fully five minutes, one day, Dinah tried the impossible, seeking to anchor the foot of a middle leg to the smooth glass of the picture frame. Her foot tapped away on the hard surface, ticking almost with the regularity of a watch.

I had had many praying mantis pets before, but Dinah was the most fearless and companionable of them all. Frequently she would perch on my desk-lamp close beside me and clean herself carefully, running her antennae through her jaws, going over each leg in turn, and finishing up by washing her face kittenwise with her forelegs.

Transcending all of Dinah's other qualities was her appetite. Night or day, she was always ready to eat. To slake her thirst, from time to time, she would bend down and drink water from a teaspoon. All praying mantises are noted for their hunger and the variety of their menus. They consume pests that range from spiny caterpillars to hard-shelled beetles. I have seen a half-grown mantis climbing a grass stem with the evident intent of capturing a Black Swallowtail butterfly, far larger than itself.

A few years ago, after I had told of my hillside garden during a radio broadcast, I received scores of letter from people who were interested in getting mantis watch-dogs for their gardens. One woman in Philadelphia wanted to know if I could send her a praying mantis to chase spiders out of her attic. An inventor in the Middle West desired a dozen of the insects for testing a death-ray!

During Dinah's lunch-time – which was as often as I could stop and catch living insects for her to devour – she would sit up with her prey clutched in her spiked forelegs. When eating red-legged locusts, katydids and long-horned grasshoppers, she suggested a man dining on sweet corn and holding the cob at both ends. Crickets she sometimes clutched in a single foreleg.

As autumn advanced, insects grew more scarce. It was then that I discovered the unusual capacities of Dinah. For a time, I fed her on bits of hamburger, corned beef and bologna to supplement the living insects. Next, some insects which had been paralysed in a jar of ammonia fumes were offered. Disregarding the fumes, she gobbled them down and smacked her palps. Later, wasps and hornets – stings, venom-sacs and all – followed in the wake of the ammonia seasoned fare. Running short of regular food one day, I fished two wasps out of a cyanide killing bottle. They were reeking with poisonous fumes. But Dinah seemed to consider them the choicest of all. I expected to see her stretched out on my desk the next morning, stiff and dead, an object lesson in gluttony. Instead, I found her waving her forelegs, turning her head from side to side, very much alive and very hungry. From then on, my conscience was clear. I fed her with whatever came to hand.

Once she ate an insect that had been packed in dichlorbenzol, that ill-smelling, moth-ball chemical used to keep dermestid beetles away from butterfly collections. True, the odor was too much for her at first. But after the atmosphere cleared a little around the proffered food, she fell to with her usual gusto. On one day, the indestructible Dinah devoured three paper-making wasps which had been killed by deadly cyanide fumes. The next day, I offered her a gastronomical superlative — a wasp which had been killed in the cyanide jar, then dipped in shellac, then soaked in 195-proof denatured alcohol. This cyanide shellac-denatured-alcohol Mickey Finn troubled her not at all. She downed it with relish and wiped her mouth and washed her face and looked around for more.

These feats resulted in Dinah, for a time, becoming the center of attention at a scientific gathering. Leaving for a meeting of the Brooklyn Entomological Society one afternoon, I slipped the indestructible mantis into my brief case. If she was thrilled by her trip on the Long Island Railroad and on subways under America's largest metropolis, she didn't show it. I suspect that her outstanding impression of the journey was the absence of edible insects amid the stone and brick and concrete of New York City.

It was on the way to the New York Public Library, that day, that Dinah had her appearance on Broadway. It was a run both in the theatrical and the physical sense. I had opened the zipper case several times during the trip to the city and each time I found the insect peering up from the bottom, its eyes brown, almost chocolate, in the gloom of the case's interior. While walking up Broadway, near Times Square, I zipped open the case again and peered in. As I

210

looked in at one side, Dinah scrambled quickly out of the other side. She teetered on the corner of the case and as I made a grab for her she shot away in a flying leap that carried her to the top of a traffic stanchion.

I looked around with the self-conscious feelings of the O. Henry character who was handed a hot-cross bun by a Russian princess who snipped off one of his coat buttons and disappeared up an alley, leaving him the centre of attention in a curious crowd. However, nobody seemed to have noticed Dinah. But as I paused, a sandwich man approached the fire-plug, stopped, and stared in surprise. A passer-by also stopped, and while I edged away and stood uncertain what to do, others paused. Soon we had a crowd.

The knot of people stared silently. Seeing a momentary thinning out of the approaching walkers, I sidled the towards, stooped quickly in an imaginary shoelace-tying and, scooping Dinah up, thrust her into a side coat pocket. With my hand over the struggling and outraged mantis I walked on until I could open the brief case and push Dinah once more inside.

In the check-room of the New York Public Library, where I left the case while I spent an hour upstairs going over some material needed for a magazine article, Dinah recovered from the excitement of her brief run on Broadway. A little later, in a restaurant, I peeked inside the case to see how the insect fared. This time, I was careful to open the zipper slide only an inch or so.

On the train going home again I chose a secluded seat and let Dinah perch on the window-sill, completely absorbed in the view as we rushed through towns and villages.

Back in my study, she seemed no worse for the journey and the attendant excitement. In fact, the only noticeable effect was a stimulation of her appetite. I left her with several crickets and a late autumn grasshopper and went to bed. The next morning she alone occupied the box. Grasshopper and crickets had merged with the mantis. But Dinah greeted me by waving her forelegs as a signal for more.

THE RESCUE

From the book "The Singing Forest"

By H. MORTIMER BATTEN

In the far north of Scotland where the red Highland deer roam freely, a laird and his gillie, MacEwen, were out on the moors inspecting the herds. They see a magnificent old stag leader – a Royal as they are called – acknowledge his newly-born son. As they watch, the calf's mother, a fine, but lame hind, surprises a vicious mountain fox who springs away, mauling the calf as she goes, so that for the rest of his life he is instantly recognized by a split ear. Disaster follows swiftly when MacEwen's dog, trained to pull down any injured or weak members of the herd, fails to see the fox and so misinterprets his master's instruction – he kills the hind. Swiftly the Royal stag returns to avenge the hind, killing the dog with one blow of his hoof. The horrified and impotent spectators are left with the tiny calf, doomed to death and too young even to be afraid of them. They decide to take him home.

On their arrival at the castle, the deer calf, Corrie, was handed over to the laird's two children; and Callum, old MacEwen's son, who acted as general factotum about the place, was called in as adviser.

213

Callum was a grave young man in his early twenties, sprung from a line that had served the family as gamekeepers for generations. His knowledge of Nature was therefore profound, his love of and loyalty to the laird and the children a matter of psychological inheritance. His judgement stood unchallenged in all matters affecting their pets; he was their adviser and guardian in most things concerning the gentler phases of their home life. At one time a goodly number of deer calves were fed on the estate, and to Callum in his early youth had fallen the task of rearing them. Therefore no better adviser could have existed.

The laird's children were Fiona, aged ten, and Alastaire, due for his big school next year. The baby, still in her crib, hardly entered the picture. On one side of the big day-nursery a circular basket was filled with heather for a bed for Corrie. Two other habitual occupants of this happy room were to prove personalities of no small standing in Corrie's life – Chang, the Pekingese, and old Bongo, the golden Labrador whom everybody loved. No sooner had Corrie drunk his first bottle of milk from Fiona's gentle hands than the fun started. Chang, who last week had worried a bantam and killed and eaten Fiona's pet pig, made it plain that he resented

this trespass of an unknown wilding upon their innermost sanctuary. He indicated that Corrie would meet the same fate as the contemptible guinea-pig if the matter were left to him, whereupon Bongo, with his higher understanding, planted himself stolidly between Corrie and Chang, and forthwith appointed himself responsible for their new pet's safety.

Not till Chang had been damped down under several cushions did the snarling and barking cease, then Corrie, in his mottled coat and revived by the warm food, took spirited possession of the floor. Within twenty minutes he and Chang were sending the mats flying in all directions on the polished floor, and so began a partnership whose strength must stand as almost unique between two animals so far apart in character and breeding.

Corrie soon outgrew the day-nursery stage, and began to show his eagerness for extended freedom. Whenever the nursery door was opened he would make a dash for it, frequently to the consternation of old Nanny with her tray of baby requirements. Thus it became customary for anyone wishing to enter the room to knock respectfully, whereupon those already there would fall upon Corrie and hold him pinioned till the door was safely closed again.

"Let him out – let him out," advised the laird. "Make him a bed in the summer-house. No sense in keeping a red deer calf cooped up indoors."

So Callum penned off a corner of the old summer-house and made a deep bed for him, and when he had established that as his home, Corrie showed his independence by using the window as a way of entrance and exit in preference to the door: if the door were left open he would immediately nose it shut. His next step was to proclaim the surrounding putting-green as undividedly his personal property, on which only a favoured few were permitted to trespass. Not even Chang was included, no one, indeed, but the two children and Callum. Other members of the household were immediately pushed and prodded till they moved off, this being one of the first of the little stag characteristics to show itself. The putting-green was

215

his terrace, and he the king stag who marshals his hinds and will admit of no intruders.

Thus a more independent phase of Corrie's life began, and quickly he responded to his freedom. Fiona's devotion and gentleness made up in his life what it lacked by his unnatural bereavement, for she was an attractive and winning little girl, and he was always restless without her. Then came rather a wide gap in the young deer's affections, till somewhat casually they embraced Alastaire, Callum, and Chang, while Bongo he regarded as grandfather of his little clan, there mainly to be sought for protection, but always to be treated respectfully. From this it will be seen that he was a pet of character, and certainly he was born with all the characteristic Highland clannishness of his kind.

Corrie's life in the garden was an exact pattern of his later life on the hill, himself an exact counterpart of his wild kindred across the river. There was a wild-deer reasoning behind all his comings and goings, and a perfectly clear explanation why he took so naturally to many of the children's games, but could never be made to play an understanding part in others. Children's games are but imaginative elaborations of the games little wild animals have played for ages past. He naturally mastered hide-and-seek so far as the seeking was concerned, but he could never grasp the hiding part of the business, since there was no eagle in the skies and no scent of fox in the air. He was glad enough to remain hidden so long as the pressure of his mistress's hand was on his head, but immediately that pressure was relaxed Corrie – like Chang – considered the uninteresting scene ended. But when it came to seeking, Corrie knew that one or more of his beloved band of playmates was missing, and he would not rest till they were restored to the party. There was no hiding from Corrie, for that little wet nose of his was a quick and certain finder.

Generally, at the most crucial moments, Chang would discover a real or imaginary cat lurking in the camp, and away he could go with flying ears and whisking tail, Corrie hard behind him. For

Corrie hated cats with a real and bitter hatred, and if he found the cat scent on one of his private deer paths, he would spend the next ten minutes beating out the shrubs and snorting through the thickets.

Corrie's infancy was slipping by with the lengthening of the summer days. He was becoming more and more headstrong, more and more disposed to overstep the narrow laws of convention to which our domestic animals submit naturally. His head was now hard; he was able to stand up on his hind-legs and strike out with his fore-legs, and a blow across a face would have left its mark.

It was Alistaire who first learnt this, for the son of the house sprang from a long line of soldier ancestors, and he held that a young wild animal which must inevitably return to its own place in life should learn to guard its own interests. So he would put on the boxing-gloves and deal Corrie a dab or two, and if Corrie refused to fight, he would very soon receive a light cuff on his split ear, which always enraged him. Up he would rear on his hind-legs, whereafter Alastaire's part consisted in warding off the thrusts of Corrie's fore-hoofs.

But one day the boy's defence failed, and he had to go to his mother with a deep cut extending from his brow to his mouth, and blood dripping from his chin. Of course he was full of excuses for Corrie, who was in no way to blame. The fault was entirely his own for having failed to ward off the blow he had deliberately invited.

"I quite understand," his mother agreed, "but in future you had better wear your fencing-mask for these engagements. Corrie is stronger now, and the fore-hoofs of deer are dangerous weapons."

The sight of Alastaire with half his face in plaster perhaps enhanced the admiration of the village boys, but it did not improve Corrie's position with their mothers. Alastaire might have lost an eye, and so might any of their small sons who went to the castle with messages. Did Madam realize that the deer calf was no longer a safe playmate for children? What a pity it would be if he scarred the bonny face of Miss Fiona! – and quite clearly Corrie should now be returned to the hill . . .

Old MacDiarmid, who attended the flower-borders surrounding the house, held kindred views; for there was nothing Corrie loved better than to catch this valued and venerable retainer bedding out his young plants. Then Corrie would approach silently and swiftly by one of his own beaten paths, and having delivered the matador's thrust would be gone ere MacDiarmid could collect himself.

But one day the old man was just too quick for him and, turning, he threw his trowel. The tool caught Corrie a clatter across his split ear, and the calf went down like a felled ox. "Oh, poor wee beastie! Poor wee beastie!" cried the old man in remorse, thinking he had slain Fiona's pet, but before he could reach the spot Corrie was up and bouncing away like a rubber ball, a creature completely demented. He leapt the wicket-gate with a foot to spare and MacDiarmid heard the rattle of his hoofs across the road, at which he returned to his work satisfied that he had taught the mischievous little varmint a lesson.

From the other side of the main road a narrow lane ran down to the sawmill which cut the estate timber and supplied the house and

221

the village with power. In an outbuilding of the old mill they kept the fishing-rods, and having put his rod away Alastaire emerged into the lane. There he saw Corrie careering towards him, his ears laid back, his eyes shining, running as he had never run before. Alastaire saw at a glance that he was "breaking", and he knew that nothing short of fire will stop a breaking sheep or deer. They have been known to throw themselves over cliffs or to shatter their limbs among the screes when in this state of blind panic. Now Corrie shot past, leaping high into the air, then raced madly on towards the river.

Not far ahead the built-in mill lade, some twenty feet across, carried half the water of the river down to the big wheel, and Corrie was racing straight towards it. When he reached its vertical brink he made no attempt to stop, but simply leapt straight out, to be whirled away by the racing waters. Here was tragedy in the making; for there was no possibility of dragging him out till the giant buckets of the wheel carried him down and tossed him across the depths of the mill pool.

Now Alastaire himself "broke" – or something very near it, for little short of fire would have stopped him. His only hope of saving Corrie lay in grabbing him immediately the great wheel emptied its buckets into the pool – or that was his wild plan. It was a matter of seconds now, and Alastaire also ran as he had never run before, passed the old mill building with its groaning wheel, then raced down the stone steps to the edge of the pool.

It was a sinister place of profound depth, and black as ink save where the pathways of foam wound across it. Alastaire knew well its terrible undercurrents, for he had taken more than one salmon from its waters. He knew that once a fish got below you the only thing was to put down your rod-tip and break him free, for he was sure to pass down the cauldron below and scream your reel empty. He waited for Corrie to appear, but the first he saw of him was when the wheel tossed him headlong across the pool like a saturated sack. But it was Corrie all right. The boy just glimpsed his big ears, then his slender hind-legs rising stiffly above the surface.

It was foolish, of course, for what was the life of a deer calf compared with that of a sound Highland boy, yet Alastaire's courage never wavered. He slipped his kilt-buckle, then struck out hand over hand across the pool. Something whispered to him, "Keep on the surface. Don't let your legs sink or you'll be sucked under."

Alastaire was a strong boy for his age and an able swimmer. Fortunately he did not see the miller's wife racing down the steps after him, nor did he hear her horrified screams. He remembered only the incredible sport of it, the fight with the currents, the triumph of catching Corrie by the collar, then the desperate fight back with his heavy load, and the first dawning of fear as he felt himself being borne irresistibly towards the mouth of the cauldron. But he did not let Corrie go.

At the very brink the old lady caught him by one arm and hung on, but she could not pull him out, so she screamed to him to let go of the deer calf. But Alastaire was deaf to her entreaties, and it was not till the miller ran down that the two were dragged from the water.

The old lady embraced the boy about the neck and dissolved into tears of thankfulness, but he said simply, "Thank you, Mary. You did well to hang on to us." He took up his tattered old kilt and re-buckled it, then turned to the miller and said, "Will you carry Corrie for me, John? I feel a bit blown after that."

The old man looked at the deer calf which had so nearly sunk his employer's son, and shook his head sadly. "No use, Master Alastaire," said he. "He went over the wheel. Every bone in his body must be broken. He's dead – quite dead!"

"Never mind," replied Alastaire. "Carry him up for me. We must take him back to my sister." So the solemn little procession went

up to the castle. Alastaire, dripping water, then old John carrying Corrie, and last of all Mary, still shedding tears of thankfulness.

They laid Corrie by the kitchen fire, where Cook covered him with a hot blanket, then Fiona came. Alastaire looked up at her defeatedly and half-accusingly. "It's no use, Fiona," he stammered, "I did my best to save him, but he went over the mill wheel, and he's dead, quite dead."

But Fiona, with eyes only for her brother, threw her eager arms about his neck. "Oh, poor Alastaire! Poor Alastaire!" she cried. "I am sure you did your very best."

Because he did not like to see the sadness of others Alastaire went away to one of those quiet corners he knew, to the Singing Forest where the great trees rubbed against each other in the wind and filled the cathedral quietude with a soothing melody. Fiona and her mother remained by the kitchen fire where soft red light cast its shadows on the pathetic little bundle within the circle of warmth, Corrie, with only his pretty little head out of the folds of the blanket with which Cook had covered him. They said nothing, because there was nothing to say, nothing to do. Callum had been in and looked at Corrie and touched his eyes, then turned away lest his manhood should fail – or rather lest his manhood should awake and overwhelm the heart of him.

Then in strolled Bongo, staring and sniffing, and thrusting his way to the fire he began to lick Corrie. Lick, lick, lick, his pink tongue went from the end of the cold little body and back again. He tried to turn him over till ready hands did it for him, and lick, lick, lick, Bongo went over the other side. Sixty minutes passed – an hour – but still Bongo licked. He never paused, never looked up from the task he had set himself. He lay down beside Corrie, one yellow paw over the little animal's shoulders as though to warm him, and still he steadily licked on. Then suddenly Fiona rose with a cry of joy. "Mummy, Mummy – he's alive," she cried. "I saw his eyelids flicker! Corrie's alive! Bongo has licked him back to life!" And she ran through the house, crying triumphantly, "Corrie's alive! Corrie's alive!"

BADGER BROCK

From the book "Die klaren Augen"

By LILLI KOENIG

Lilli Koenig and her husband Otto have spent their lives looking after and writing about animals. As wardens of a nature reserve they are often called upon to take strange pets into their household or to rear deserted baby animals like Badger Brock about whom we hear here.

Brock was a proper little badger – and at the same time he was a companion as good as any you could possibly wish for. But let me tell you the story from the beginning just as it happened.

It was a beautiful spring morning and a man came to our door. He was holding one arm protectively over one side of his jacket, and there was a very good reason for this because underneath that side of the jacket was a small, gray, trembling bundle. The man was a keeper from Schönbrunn, and the little bundle was Brock, who had just been taken away from his honest Schönbrunn badger mother. And we – my husband, our son Otto, and I – were being appointed step-mother and father on the spot.

Brock was hardly as big as a half-grown rabbit. His fur was grey and rough, his paws were black and stumpy, his ears lay close to his head, and he had small, round eyes as black as coal in a plump baby face – and the whole of him was a bundle of misery in a dreary world. Of course, the first thing we did was to offer him the bottle – as you do with sucklings. But he just screwed his face up into folds and closed his little eyes tightly. It was clear that he wanted to have nothing to do with us or the rest of the world. That wasn't altogether surprising, so we gave him time. But by evening, our Brock hadn't taken one single drop of milk. He slept almost all the time and we began to feel a little depressed and worried about the little bundle of misery we had taken on, which now lay there so pathetically helpless and lonely. There must be some way of getting through to him, but how? The bottle he had refused to touch lay there with

226

the milk still in it, and that gave us an idea, and as he slept we gently and cautiously pushed the rubber teat between his lips. And, lo and behold! in his sleep he began to pull away at the warm milk. That lowered the barrier, and the next day he was keen about eating, and clung to the bottle with his forepaws and sucked away avidly. Brock was in good fettle again and all his misery was gone. Badgers are tough creatures.

Before long he began to wander around and explore the room, leaving small pools which he seemed to be distributing in some sort of even pattern. However, by this time we were so taken with our little guest that we found this amusing. Now he began to follow us around, making noises – a short of low, quick grunting that sounded as though he were scolding us for something. We soon learned that he was asking to be picked up and carried. If you didn't pick him up at once, then the low, growling grunt changed into a higher-pitched, imperative indignation – that usually did the trick.

He was never at a loss to amuse himself, though. He played around like a puppy, his eyes excitedly sparkling with a dangerous fire. His incisors were like small, sharp, glistening white daggers, and in his play he would take a delight in fastening them into our calves. Eventually, although it was summer and hot, we found we must go around in knee-length boots all the time, for protection. He didn't much care for that – it spoiled one of his favourite games. But, as he grew more, in no time at all he was able to spring up to the hollow behind the knee, above the boots. One shouldn't judge animals by human standards, but even with this salutary principle in mind I can't help feeling that he positively enjoyed the shriek that followed when his attack was sucessful.

We were beginning to be puzzled though, and with good reason: Brock was growing rapidly and vigorously, yet he firmly refused to take any solid food. In fact, he hadn't even yet learned to take his milk out of a bowl – and when we tried him with it his efforts were ridiculous; he would just sneeze into the milk, get it up his nose and cough – but despite all his efforts he succeeded in drinking none of it, so he had to stick to the bottle.

And then something strange happened. Five of our turkey chicks were marching in single file over the grass one day, when suddenly there were only four. I was astonished. I had hardly let them out of my sight, and I looked around, puzzled to think where the fifth could have got to. And there was Brock, sitting on his hindquarters, his eyes glistening like two diamonds. And between his front paws was the missing turkey chick, its head bitten off, playing its role of dinner long before Christmas. Indignantly I ran towards Brock to take away his prey; but he growled threateningly, the hairs on his back grew stiff and his paws held still more firmly onto his booty. My anger disappeared like snow in the spring sunshine. Instead, I stood there and marvelled. This wasn't our little suckling Brock any more. It was a wild animal, acting as nature and instinct directed him – a wild little predator skilfully dismembering my turkey chick before my eyes with obvious experience until finally nothing remained but the wings and the claws. I realized that play had become reality. Our Brock was becoming – had become – a badger. After that he didn't get the bottle any more.

To cut a long story short, in the following weeks we lost a guinea pig and a coot, and just in time succeeded in saving the life of our tame purple heron.

Then one day he attacked another heron, and that was too much. We decided that Brock must go. We were so determined that we got rid of him that very day. His new owner received him with enthusiasm, so we felt we needn't worry, even from Brock's point of view, about deciding to banish him.

But the house was strangely empty now that Brock was no longer there – and almost sad. In fact it *was* sad, because we missed Brock's black-and-white snout pushing open the doors; because the wooden box in the corner was empty, and because the much-bitten rubber ball was lying there, lonely. However, within three days Brock's new owner and master was back with him, in a box under his arm. He opened it and out rolled Brock and greeted me with enthusiasm and a joyful reunion bite in the calf. It turned out that in his new home Brock had very quickly dispensed with a couple of rabbits and a tame white rat. In addition, the half a dozen hens – scared out of their wits no doubt – had gone on an egg strike. So Brock was returned with thanks. It was difficult to say who was the more delighted – Brock or us.

After that he stayed with us and dug himself entrances into the basement space under our house. We could often hear him rummaging about below our feet; sometimes beneath the kitchen floor, sometimes underneath the workroom. We had a rather disagreeable feeling that he might be undermining the foundations of the roof over our heads, and we began to imagine fearfully what might happen. We could see the walls beginning to buckle and the roof to subside. Just the same, we enjoyed having him back, and we resumed our playful give-and-take relationship.

It wasn't long after his return that one day Brock disappeared, and was nowhere to be found. And once again we realized, as we had realized before when we had given him away, how quiet and lonely the house was without its familiar pest. Two days later, the stoker from the near-by sanatorium arrived with the laconic information: "There's a wild beast loose in our cellar." As we are known to be passionately interested in all kinds of animals, wild or tame, we went along with him at once to investigate. There was plenty of evidence in support of what he said: the cellar looked as though a band of small devils had been at work in it! Bins were

overturned, torn paper and bits of ripped cardboard were scattered all over the floor, paint cans had been opened and spilled, and a high pile of fire-logs had been pulled apart. Sure enough, as we came in, Brock's black-and-white head rose up slowly out of a basket in the corner. The stoker grinned at our obvious delight, and Brock was very glad to see us, but behaved himself as good as gold, his gentle mood obviously induced by a long and involuntary fast.

What had happened seemed fairly clear: in his nightly wanderings he must have come across the small window of the cellar and fallen through it in his inquisitiveness, then been unable to climb out again. So now we had him back again we continued to sigh under his tyranny – but knew well that we didn't really want to lose him.

Autumn slowly approached and our Brock grew bigger and fatter, and more and more busy under our house. Night after night we heard him carrying bundles of twigs and leaves into our foundations. He would carry a large bundle tightly clasped in his front paws and work his way backwards under the house. Then you would hear him scraping and digging for hours on end. On one occasion we felt quite certain that our kitchen floor was settling under our feet. Something was obviously going on and one day we thought it was about time we discovered just what, so we sawed a hole in the timber facing that surrounded the foundations of our house, then wriggled through it on our bellies – having wisely enticed Brock out beforehand and put him safely under lock and key. In the light of our torch we looked around us. There were the timber supports of our house at regular intervals, still standing firmly, and there were innumerable spiders' webs and mouse holes – but no sign of a badger set.

Then we found an enormous pile of twigs, straw and leaves – and in the centre was a track suit we had been missing for some time. There was also a gnawed doormat, one missing slipper, a pair of woollen socks and a teacloth. This was Brock's badger set! But nowhere was there any sign of the tunnel system we had feared to find was undermining our foundations. There were just one or two shallow pits near the nest that were obviously being used for hygienic purposes. Relieved, we wriggled our way back into the light and boarded up the hole behind us.

There was nothing to fear in that respect. But there was plenty to fear otherwise, because Brock was almost full-grown now; and his incisors were like sharp swords. In addition, he was becoming increasingly playful, and he would pursue us with such excessively robust proofs of his affection that more than once blood flowed – our blood, because unfortunately our thin hides were no match for his sharp teeth.

We would be sitting there peacefully in the evening, reading or writing, when suddenly the outside wall would shudder under an enormous thump, followed by another, and another. We knew what *that* was: Brock wanted to come in and play with us. Not being let in at once, he tried butting at the door, which threatened to give under the assault of his powerful body and clever front paws. And we could hear a rolling, grumbling sound deep down in his throat, which meant that Brock was getting a little annoyed at not being invited in. Should we, or shouldn't we? I went to the window, and

Brock was there in a moment, swinging on the solidly fastened flower box and scolding us. Hurriedly we brought a short ladder and put it outside against the window to see whether he could climb up it – it wasn't more than three or four feet high. Immediately he rose on his hind legs and pulled the ladder about a bit, and after a while – it may have been five minutes – he climbed onto the first rung, fell off, scolding angrily, and then tried again with determination. After perhaps another five minutes he had managed it, and fell with a thump into the room. "Bravo Brock! You could earn your living in a circus," we praised him.

He seemed starved for play, and began to romp so violently that I jumped onto the table, to rescue myself – strange behaviour isn't at all unusual amongst human beings who are devoted to animals! But despite my urgent warnings, my Otto decided to join Brock's gaiety, and have it out with Brock this time. From my place of safety I watched developments. First of all Otto rolled up his sleeves, and squared up to the delighted badger. Then the fight started. It might have looked brutal, but Otto was really only on the defensive, and, of course, Brock could have retreated at any time. But he had no such intention. He lowered his head to protect his nose and met the rain of blows with his powerful neck and shoulders. When Otto paused for breath for a moment, Brock leaned affectionately against him with all his weight, then suddenly took a nip at his calf. After about a quarter of an hour of this Otto was quite exhausted and had to give in. It was a clear victory for Brock, and his eyes sparkled with delight. It was very obvious throughout the whole encounter that Brock never forgot for one moment that it was all just a friendly rough and tumble.

As time passed, Brock had grown so much that I hardly dared to go out of the house, if I thought he could see me – and Brock was almost constantly outside, besieging our door, trying to get in for a romp. I must honestly confess that sometimes I stood there for a while with mild goose flesh before I dared venture forth. There were various possibilities: I could try to take him by surprise, jump over him and race on without bothering to close the door behind me as one ought. Or I could perhaps let him come in, then slip out hastily, slamming the door on him. But that was rather a desperate measure with him. I usually took the simplest and most peaceable – but also the most arduous – course. First of all I would let him spring at my feet when I came out, and then I would bend down swiftly and pick him up by the neck. He was still very fond of being carried, and his tense muscles would relax and he would lie in my arms, belly upwards, his eyes half closed, and let me carry him like a paschal lamb. Unfortunately, by now he weighed well over twenty pounds, and the path from our door was definitely uphill. But it made him so happy, I felt I must occasionally indulge him.

That January we had a lot of snow, and Brock stayed prudently outside in his nest, but we were very interested – and anxious – to know how he would behave and manage in the snow, particularly as we had found the tracks of another badger in the snow a little distance away. At one time it was believed that badgers were true hibernating animals, and that they remained comatose in their sets for the greater part of the winter without taking any food, but more modern research has shown that this is not so. When the weather is bad, the badger certainly stays in his set and lives on his own accumulated fat, but there is no question of any material drop in body temperature as there is, for example, with the marmot or dormouse. So one fine afternoon we enticed him out of his nest and carried him down to the edge of the wood, where the snow was a couple of feet deep. As soon as we put him down he turned round and made off home along the track we had left behind us. But we ran after him, picked him up again and flung him without more ado into the soft snow, to see how he would manage. At first

he tried to hold his head above it and wade forward like a poor swimmer out of his depth, but that didn't work very well. He didn't make much progress, so he tried a new method. He put his head down into the snow and worked his way forward like a snow plough. At this he made good progress, but soon was obviously unhappy and quite exhausted, so we hadn't the heart to make any further experiments. We picked him up and carried him home to the warm fire, where we warmed his almost hairless belly. At least we now had a fairly shrewd idea as to why badgers stay in their set in winter – they have such short, stumpy legs it is difficult for them to make progress in deep snow.

When spring arrived Brock began to be missing for longer and longer periods, and his nightly wanderings took him farther and farther away. He had abandoned the nest under our house now and was sleeping in some place unknown to us. When we walked through the wood in the evening he would occasionally turn up still and amble along beside us, but less and less often. And then came the day, we later realized, on which we saw him for the last time. Had he built himself a set somewhere, or wandered off altogether – or had he come to grief in some way? We never knew. One memory he left behind: of all the animals both large and small that had ever lived with us and looked up at us with candid, loving eyes, Brock was the most lovable, despite his delight in nipping at our legs. And everyone who got to know him was ready to confirm that verdict.

THE GOSHAWK

From the book of the same title

By T. H. WHITE

The training of the young goshawk is an arduous business demanding the constant and complete attention of the trainer over a long period. The incident related here took place fairly early but a very close relationship had already been formed between the man and the bird.

We were back again in the stage of manning the hawk to the outside world, a stage which entailed carrying him on the fist all day. It was possible sometimes to relieve the tedium of these day-long vigils by taking him fishing at Black Pits, where, in the effort to deceive the subtlety of those large, sly carp which had probably been introduced there by the monks of Luffield Abbey, it was possible to roll two patiences into one. By tying a string to the first joint of the fishing rod (a string whose other end could be held between the teeth), it was possible to fish one-handed, while the hawk sat on the other, and we did at one time or another kill two fish of about a pound each.

But the amusing thing was that on this Monday, on a spontaneous motion, Gos accepted his first bath. There was a little puddly backwater off the main stew, and in it a heavy board with a nail driven through. I paddled out and tied the leash to the nail, then introduced Gos to the board. He did not want to stand on it at first, for it was low and strange, but soon – ancestrally – he almost twigged. You could see the racial unconscious voice speaking to his bird brain in parables. With an arrogant and dainty motion he stepped onto the board.

Gos cocked his head on one side and stared at the water. Odd, he seemed to be saying to himself – probably dangerous, but yet I like it. What *is* it? He put in his beak, leaning forward with every precaution, to see what it tasted of. (Hawks were one of the few creatures which did not regularly drink water except as a laxative; none needed to be provided for them in the mews.) It did not taste of anything, so he put in his beak again. Curious. He looked over his shoulder at the bigger bit of the stuff behind him, roused his

235

feathers with a rattle, inspected the reeds, the landing stage, me motionless. He thought of flying to the landing stage, less than a yard away, and then gave up the idea. He walked down the slope of the plank into the water. All the time I did not know whether he would accept a bath or not.

Gos stopped in about an eighth of an inch of water and looked at his reflected toes. He bit one of them to see if it was there. When he saw that it was there he diverted his attention and bit some of the water. He then bit his jesses and the plank, at points where both of them were wet. It was exceedingly strange.

Gos slipped on the wet plank, with an undignified lurch, went into quite half an inch of water, and hurried back to recover his composure. He bit his toe again. It was rather nice.

With the utmost caution he walked down the plank again and considered the possibility of stepping off into two inches. It was evidently a rash step; so he merely made a pass at it with one leg, withdrawing the talon pensively half-way through.

Gos generally looked terrible, terrible in the sense that an eagle or a vulture has such a look. In the strong sunlight which shone on the lake – at last the weather was pretending to turn for haymaking – he certainly looked beautiful. But the cruelty had gone out of his aspect. He was only a funny and silly little Gos, whose transparent mind showed him to be an infant still, as it struggled with the elements of hydrostatics.

The sun shone on him, giving him a blue nimbus round his head. The cere flesh about his nostrils was supposedly yellow, as were the irises of his eyes. But that luminous eye (his main feature; it glared out, a focus to all the rest of him, from under frowning brows, the optic of an insane assassin) was genuinely luminous, like the paint on the hands of a wrist watch. Luminous paint, phosphorus: it was blue really, just as much as it was yellow. So the sunlight on Gos took a blue tinge from the hairy whiskers which he wore about his cere and eyelid, carried it on to the eye itself, haloed the whole head in a tint exquisitely elusive, of bird flesh – neither blue nor yellow.

236

Gos concentrated his attention backwards, without looking round, and dipped the tip of his tail in the extraordinary medium. It was fun. He stood and considered the matter, rousing his feathers again. When he roused he looked exactly like a fir-cone. In other manifestations he sometimes would hunch himself up like a penguin, when he was hungry, or go soft like an owl, when he was sleepy.

Now, taking me so much by surprise that I could scarcely keep from laughing, the absurd princeling blew out all his feathers, lifted his tail in the air, and, like an old lady sitting down in a tram or lifting

her bustle to get at a purse among the petticoats, sat down suddenly, shiftily, luxuriously, in the puddle. I had never seen a bird sit down before, for the gesture was quite unlike the laying hen's. With ludi-

crous rapture Gos squatted in the puddle, got up, and putting his head between his legs, looked at himself from underneath. It was the concentration of attention backward, the strange mixture of pride and affection and anxiety for these parts, the ungainly and somewhat private motion with which he immersed the proud posterior: it was these, and the indignity. The infant Tarquin had suddenly become a charlady at Margate.